cape town planetariu

starwatching
a southern hemisphere guide to the galaxy

Nov

10

31

10

ep

20

30

Anthony Fairall
ILLUSTRATIONS BY MARGIE WALTER AND HERSCHEL MAIR

iziko
museums of cape town

Planetarium, Iziko Museums of Cape Town
PO Box 61, Cape Town 8000

For Lara, Richard, David, Desmond and Elizabeth

Struik Publishers
(a division of New Holland Publishing
(South Africa) (Pty) Ltd)
Cornelius Struik House, 80 McKenzie Street, Cape Town 8001, South Africa
New Holland Publishing is a member of the Johnnic Publishing Group
www.struik.co.za
Log on to our photographic website **www.imagesofafrica.co.za** for an African experience.

First published in 2002 by Struik Publishers
1 3 5 7 9 10 8 6 4 2

Publishing manager: Pippa Parker
Editor: Helen de Villiers
Design director: Janice Evans
Designer: Lesley Mitchell
Cover design: Lesley Mitchell and Herschel Mair
Reproduction by Hirt & Carter Cape (Pty) Ltd
Printed and bound by Craft Print (Pte) Ltd, Singapore

ISBN 1 86872 738 6

Introduction

There could be no better place to start this book than under the night skies of the Karoo, atop the plateau of the South African Astronomical Observatory. Although it is no more than 1 800 metres above sea level, somehow one feels closer to the stars, which seem to blaze like jewels.

Over to the northwest, there happen (at the time of writing) to be three bright planets, Venus, Jupiter and Saturn. Venus is so bright that one can make out the faintest of shadows cast by its light. High overhead is the distinctive pattern of stars labelled, long ago, Orion the hunter. Towards the south, lying on its side is the Southern Cross. Celestial groupings have been likened to a wide variety of objects, such as dragons, dogs and ships. But they are simply imaginary pictures in the sky.

It is not surprising that imaginations run riot in this celestial realm, for its scale and beauty invite conjecture and fantasy. For centuries, the Europeans supposed that the heavens were a set of nested crystalline spheres rotated by angels. Today, the spheres and angels have vanished, to be replaced by an understanding of the sky based on science, knowledge that has only been accumulated in the most recent centuries. Correctly interpreting what is up there gives a greater sense of awe and wonder than was ever possible in days of old. That is the purpose and the reward of modern-day astronomy.

As the night progresses, so the sky above changes. By the time that our night under the stars in the Karoo has stretched to the early morning hours, the whole sky seems to have turned. The Southern Cross now stands upright. Orion – and even the three bright planets – have set below the horizon. But planets Mars and Mercury have risen. Mars, which has a distinctive reddish colour, appears against the constellation of Scorpius, not far from a similarly coloured star called Antares (meaning the 'rival of Mars'). In truth, however, Mars is in the foreground and can hardly rival Antares – a gigantic, distant, swollen red giant star.

Scorpius is set against the Milky Way. Without any Moon in the sky (since it happens to be around New Moon), the stretch of the Milky Way from around the Southern Cross to Scorpius is a sight to behold. No wonder, it is part of a city of perhaps a million million stars! It is our Galaxy.

Our view of the universe – with the naked eye – does not go much further. We can just make out the Magellanic Clouds, which resemble two patches of the Milky Way that have broken away. They are, in fact, small companion galaxies to our own star system.

Star trails above a telescope of the South African Astronomical Observatory at Sutherland. The camera shutter has been left open for many hours, during which the turning of the Earth has caused the sky to appear to turn above, so creating star trails.

But here in the Karoo, at the South African Astronomical Observatory, are powerful telescopes. Each night, astronomers are privileged to use them to look – not only at our own Galaxy – but at other galaxies. And there are billions! Our city of stars is repeated many times over.

It leaves our Earth as a pale blue dot (as Carl Sagan so aptly put it), nothing more than a tiny planet circling an inconspicuous sun on the fringe of a galaxy, just one of millions in a great cosmic labyrinth. But this daunting perspective cannot diminish our real view of planet Earth – it is nevertheless home. Whatever we may think about the universe, it is after all where we live.

If this book has a purpose, it is to make you feel at home in the universe, in two ways. One is to show you where we are and what the universe is really like. The other is to encourage you to get out under the night sky and have a look for yourself.

After all, astronomy is looking up!

CHAPTER 1

Get to know your universe

A starry night sky – such as described in the introduction to this book, and viewed with eyes that have become adapted to the dark – is one of the grandest spectacles of nature. But in modern life, where most of us live in cities, or close to towns or cities, few people get to enjoy the splendours of a beautiful dark sky.

Not only can our eyes never get fully dark-adapted in a city, but much of the polluting light of urban development shines or scatters upwards, brightens the background sky, and so diminishes the brighter stars and smothers the fainter ones.

Over the past half century, light pollution has increased dramatically. Witness the accounts of old-timers who saw Halley's comet in 1910, compared with those who only just managed to see it in 1986. Up to 30 years ago, most major telescopes in southern Africa were in Johannesburg, Cape Town and Bloemfontein. Today, using a telescope from one of those cities is almost laughable. The number of stars you can count when looking skywards from your back yard is gradually diminishing.

In reality it is, of course, the naked-eye view of the universe in which, and in when, we find ourselves. To be able to see the universe around us, it is essential to get as far away as possible from light – and to be patient. Our eyes have evolved to the extent that it takes them 40 minutes – the typical duration of twilight – to become completely adapted to darkness.

It is therefore ironic that the best way to see a starry sky if you live in a city is to visit the planetarium. The light level in the planetarium auditorium allows your eyes to become fully dark-adapted, and presentations are deliberately long enough for that to come about. The planetarium's star projector is designed to show the stars at the same brightness with which they shine in the real night sky. You can see far fainter stars in

The imaginary Celestial Sphere

Many old civilisations – from the Babylonians to the Zulus – believed that there was a dome stretched over the Earth. On this dome, the stars and heavenly bodies moved. Illustrations of this concept, such as the charming one shown below, abound in literature.

Above A woodcut depicting the Celestial Sphere.

Today, of course, we know better. After all, none of the rockets we have sent out into space has gone 'clunk' into the limit of a Celestial Sphere! But the concept of representing the sky by an imaginary Celestial Sphere, centred on the Earth, is a very useful one.

Just as there is a North Pole, South Pole and Equator on our terrestrial sphere, so there is a North Celestial Pole, a South Celestial Pole and a Celestial Equator on its celestial counterpart. In fact, astronomers use a system of latitude and longitude to fix star positions on the Celestial Sphere.

Right The imaginary Celestial Sphere surrounds the Earth. Extending the Earth's axis and Equator into space fixes the Celestial Poles and Equator.

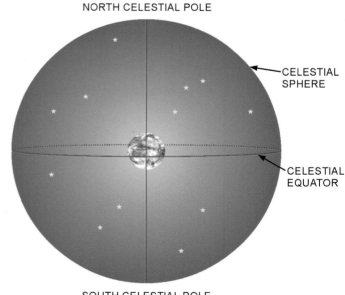

NORTH CELESTIAL POLE

CELESTIAL SPHERE

CELESTIAL EQUATOR

SOUTH CELESTIAL POLE

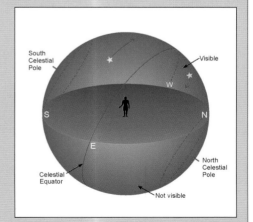

When, standing on the surface of the Earth, we look at the night sky, we can obviously look only up and not down. Consequently, we see only half of the Celestial Sphere. As to which half that is – the answer varies according to our latitude on Earth. The diagrams below illustrate the point.

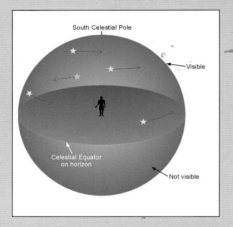

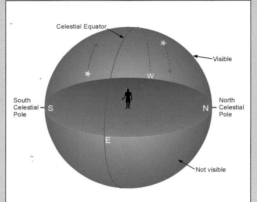

Left If you live at the Equator, the Celestial Equator will pass overhead, and the Celestial Poles will coincide with the north and south points on the horizon. As the Earth turns, and the Celestial Sphere appears to rotate, the entire sphere will eventually be seen.

Above If you live at the South Pole, you will always have the South Celestial Pole directly overhead, and the Celestial Equator on the horizon. You will never see stars north of the Celestial Equator as they are below your horizon. As the Earth turns, the Celestial Sphere appears to rotate, pivoting about the Celestial Pole overhead.

Right If you live in the southern hemisphere, the South Celestial Pole will be elevated above the southern horizon. You will see almost all the Celestial Sphere as the Earth rotates, except for a portion surrounding the North Celestial Pole, which will be permanently below your horizon. Correspondingly, there will be a portion surrounding the South Celestial Pole that will never set.

a planetarium than you can from anywhere in or near a city. But, as good as the artificial sky may be, it is still not the real thing.

Given that almost all celestial objects appear to us as no more than points of light, interpreting what we see is not easy. We do know, nevertheless, that the majority of points of light are stars, and that every star we see is a sun, much like our Sun.

It is a great pity that the English language does not use the same word for 'star' and 'sun' – it would have prevented much confusion. But it is no wonder that the word 'star' is applied to a small, round shape with points radiating out from it, for this is how we see these gently twinkling objects in the night sky. Of course, real stars are round like our Sun, and huge.

Not quite stars

Not quite everything that looks like a star in the night sky is really a star. Five fellow planets within our Solar System are visible to the naked eye, and appear as very bright stars. Venus is sometimes dubbed the 'evening star', when it is not a star at all.

A more extreme misuse of the word 'star' is evident in the term 'shooting stars' – which in reality are little pebble-sized fragments colliding with the Earth's atmosphere and being incinerated about 100 kilometres above the ground. Shooting stars, like planets, are part of our Solar System, centred on the Sun, our nearest star.

Relative sizes and distances

When compared with the general population of stars, our Sun is relatively small – it is described as a dwarf – and it is not particularly bright. Yet, from our perspective, it certainly looks like the brightest object in the sky. The problem is that when we look up into the night sky, not only can we not tell how big the stars really are, but nor can we even gauge how far away they are.

Extremely luminous stars that outshine our Sun a hundred thousand times can be so distant that they appear as faint pinpoints of light. The brightest stars in our skies appear so, either because they are relatively near to us (for example Sirius, the brightest star in our night sky) or because, in spite of being extremely distant, they are intrinsically very bright, such as the central star in Orion's Belt.

Correspondingly, the faintest stars might be so because they are too far away – or because they are intrinsically very dim, even though relatively close by. Thus, in spite of being the nearest star to our Solar System, Proxima Centauri (part of the Alpha Centauri system) is so intrinsically dim that it is a hundred times too faint to be seen with the naked eye. The vast majority of celestial objects are simply invisible to the naked eye, and even the strongest telescopes can help detect only a tiny fraction of the stars in our Galaxy.

Your cosmic address

The intergalactic mail service has yet to get off the ground, but cosmically minded citizens may nevertheless feel that their postal addresses could be stretched to bigger things, and to places you might not have known existed. For example:

A Fairall
59 Albion Rd
Rondebosch
Cape Town
Western Province
South Africa
Africa
Earth
Solar System
Orion Arm
Milky Way Galaxy
Local Group
Virgo Supercluster
Centaurus Wall
The Cosmos

If some of this is new to you, then chapter 3 should sort things out.

Do the stars influence our lives?

Always hoping for better things to come, many people consult astrology columns, or may even go so far as to have their complete horoscope cast. Yet astrology is a system that rests entirely on belief, without any scientific support whatsoever.

It comes from Babylonian times, when the seven moving heavenly bodies (Sun, Moon, Mercury, Venus, Mars, Jupiter and Saturn) were believed to be gods roaming in the sky. To this day, the planets still carry the names of ancient gods. These gods were thought to interact with the 'mysterious' star patterns that were apparently fixed on the Celestial Sphere, and so influence life on Earth. More particularly, their configuration at the moment of birth – but somehow not before or afterwards – was thought to mould an individual's character.

The most powerful 'god' was believed to be the Sun, and a person's Sun sign – the constellation in which the Sun was positioned on their date of birth – the overriding influence. From this have come the 12 well-known signs of the Zodiac and their associated dates. Most people reading this book will know their sign of the Zodiac.

Today, of course, we know that the Sun and planets are not gods. Our Earth is a planet, the Sun is a star, and the stars are distant suns. There is no reason to suppose that they control our lives any more than do the trees or the mountains.

Furthermore, modern astrology still uses the constellation dates relating to the Sun's apparent position in 500 BC. Since then, the slow wobble of the Earth's axis has shifted the dates, but the astrologers have not adapted to this. So if your horoscope is not working out, perhaps you need to be re-classified!

Somewhat with tongue-in-cheek, here are the current dates of the annual movement of the Sun against the starry constellations, which ought to tell you your true sign of the Zodiac!

Jan 20 – Feb 15	Capricornus
Feb 16 – Mar 11	Aquarius
Mar 12 – Apr 20	Pisces
Apr 21 – May 13	Aries
May 14 – Jun 21	Taurus
Jun 22 – Jul 20	Gemini
Jul 21 – Aug 10	Cancer
Aug 11 – Sep 16	Leo
Sep 17 – Oct 31	Virgo
Nov 1 – Nov 23	Libra
Nov 24 – Nov 29	Scorpius
Nov 30 – Dec 17	Ophiuchus
Dec 18 – Jan 19	Sagittarius

(Astrologers refer to 'Capricorn' and 'Scorpio', and completely overlook the constellation of Ophiuchus, the doctor of antiquity.)

Below Some constellations of the Zodiac

City of stars

What we see in the night sky is therefore a three-dimensional distribution of stars ranging from incredibly luminous to exceedingly dim – both apparently and intrinsically. But, of course, we cannot see the sky in three dimensions – not at stellar distances, anyway.

The stars we see are the central bodies of other solar systems, whose planets are far, far too faint to see. There must be solar system after solar system out there. In their billions, these solar systems make up our Milky Way, a city of a million, million stars.

Not only are there billions of stars in our galaxy, but there are billions of galaxies dotting the cosmos. We cannot see them with the naked eye, but we know they are there.

The city of stars in which we live, our Galaxy, is an immense flattened disc. Its diameter is about a hundred million times greater than that of our Solar System, a figure almost too astronomical to assimilate. Put in another way, if our Galaxy were the size of Johannesburg, the Solar System would be about a millimetre across and it would lie somewhere in the vicinity of Sandton.

We are far from the centre of the Galaxy, but we lie in the flattened disc, so the Galaxy appears to encircle us as the band of the Milky Way. The constellation of Scorpius lies in the direction of the central bulge of the Galaxy; indeed the Milky Way in the sky is much broader there. The view towards the centre is not too clear; it is obscured by thick clouds of dust floating between the stars. It has nevertheless been possible to map our Galaxy from radio waves (from cold hydrogen gas in the Galaxy), and from this map we know that our Galaxy shows a spiral pattern in its disc (see diagram alongside).

We know that galaxies tend to congregate in what are called large-scale structures – in much the same way that humans tend to gather into large crowds, but on an absolutely enormous scale. Our Galaxy's position is hardly one of any prominence: we lie towards the edge of a great crowd of galaxies known as the Virgo Super-cluster, itself a protrusion from the larger Centaurus Wall. More will be said about this in chapters 3 and 8.

Finally, in chapters 3 and 9, we shall penetrate right to the boundary of our visible universe.

The probable appearance of our Galaxy and the position of our Solar System

Flat on

OUR SOLAR SYSTEM

Edge on

OUR SOLAR SYSTEM

CHAPTER 2

Astronomical heritage and tradition

Astronomy today builds on a great heritage going back thousands of years. That heritage involves beliefs and meanings concerning the Sun, the Moon and the objects visible in the starry sky. Ignorant of the true nature of stars, fertile minds conjured up all sorts of mystical and mythological creatures said to be residing in the cosmos.

The Sun rules

The Sun was paramount: after all, our existence on Earth is so obviously dependent upon it. It gives light and warmth, it is at the heart of the chemical processes that support growth – it is not surprising that so many ancient cultures looked upon it as a god, and worshipped it accordingly. The daily cycle of the Sun, the alternation between light and dark, controls our patterns of wakefulness and sleep. We know that even relatively sophisticated cultures like the ancient Mexicans made human sacrifices to ensure that the Sun would always rise.

The annual cycle of the Sun – the variation from summer to winter – was also influential. Most ancient civilisations were aware of the extreme positions of the Sun. The Zulus, for example, talked about the 'turning back' of the Sun at the time of the solstices of midwinter or midsummer. Many civilisations also realised that these could be established by following the rising point of the Sun as it oscillated along the eastern horizon. Monumental structures such as Stonehenge in England were aligned with the solstice rising. Solstices were consequently occasions for celebration. The Swazis hold the Ncwala festival at midsummer, while the midwinter

solstice in the northern hemisphere provides the date for Christmas, and accounts for the yuletide tree and log as symbols of rebirth that predated the Christian era.

A domed sky

Both Babylonians and Zulus – if not the majority of older civilisations – saw the sky as a dome that stretched over the Earth. The Sun, Moon, planets and stars moved on the inside surface of that dome. The ancient Greeks, perhaps the first civilisation to make scholastic endeavours into the nature of the universe, saw the stars fixed on a Celestial Sphere (see box in chapter 1), a convenient but erroneous concept. Their obsession with spheres was passed to the Arabic world, and much later to Europe; the Earth was thought to be surrounded by a network of smoothly turning crystalline spheres that carried the planets, enclosed within the Celestial Sphere.

The Catholic Church adopted this geocentric universe; to dispute it was considered heresy. In 16th century Europe, there was great consternation when Copernicus (1473–1543) promoted a heliocentric model, with the Sun in the centre and the planets circling it. Giordano Bruno (1548–1600), an Italian philosopher and Dominican monk, was burnt to death for adopting the Copernican theory. Copernicus had escaped by publishing only from his deathbed, but Galileo Galilei (1564–1642), who also promoted the heliocentric model, was brought to trial and sentenced to spend the remainder of his life under 'house arrest' (a verdict only very recently overturned by

The Egyptian pyramids

There is a strong connection between the planning and positioning of the pyramids, built as tombs for the Pharaohs of Egypt, and the sky above. To ancient Egyptians, the cardinal points of the compass were of particular significance. The Sun and stars appeared to die in the west and were reborn in the east; for that reason all the pyramids were built on the western side of the Nile. The four faces of all the ancient Egyptian pyramids turn exactly towards north, south, east and west. Yet the Egyptians never recognised a spherical Earth with North and South Poles. Instead they saw a North Pole in the sky (the North Celestial Pole) around which stars never set. Almost every pyramid has an internal passage that is slanted up in the direction of that Celestial Pole, apparently linking the dead Pharaoh to the 'Imperishables', those stars that never died.

The most complex astronomical involvement lies with the largest of all the pyramids, the Great Pyramid of Khufu (Cheops). It is the most precisely aligned, only a twentieth of a degree from true north-south. Its internal layout includes four shafts slanted upwards, apparently to guide the Pharaohs' 'ka' (spirit) up to appropriate parts of the sky. All the shafts are oriented in a north-south direction (the north-south line in the sky). At the time the pyramid was built (2500 BC), these four shafts aligned with the crossing points of various significant stars: the star grouping we call Orion was believed to represent the Egyptian deity Osiris; Sirius (brightest star in the night sky) represented his consort Isis; Thuban was the 'pole' star at the time; and Khochab a bright star near the North Celestial Pole. Wobbling of the Earth's axis, known as precession, means that these alignments are no longer precisely on course.

A claim has been made by the authors Graham Hancock and Robert Bauval that the line of three pyramids at Giza represents the three bright stars in Orion's Belt, orientated as it was in 10500 BC. However, the claim is not supported by scholarly Egyptologists, while this author has noted that the orientation at that time would have been off by some ten degrees.

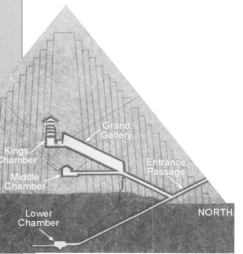

Above right The three pyramids at Giza. That furthest from the camera – the Great Pyramid of Khufu – is in fact the largest of the three.

Above Internal layout of the Great Pyramid of Khufu – the shafts point to significant stars (adapted from a diagram supplied by Hansen Planetarium).

Pope John Paul II). In short, the removal of the Earth from the centre of the universe caused much upheaval. By contrast, the later removal of the Sun from the centre of the universe during the 18th century, and the recognition of numerous 'island universes', or other galaxies (confirmed by Edwin Hubble in 1924), passed quietly.

A common, naked-eye view

The common factor we share with ancient civilisations is the naked-eye view of the night sky. When almost every celestial object appears as a pinpoint of light, it is not surprising that interpretations were often misguided. Aside from the five (slowly) moving planets, the motion of the stars is far too slow to perceive, even over thousands of years. So we see much the same sky as did ancient civilisations. Where tonight we see a triangle of stars, so too did the ancients. Where there is a pair of stars, so too did the ancients see a pair. Thus familiarity with the stars leads to familiarity with the patterns they make. Within those patterns one can identify individual stars.

We know from the Greek constellations, still recognised for convenience today, that the civilisations of Europe and of the Middle East chose patterns large enough to allow pictures to be imagined, some obvious, many requiring considerable imagination. Their names have endured for millennia. By contrast, Chinese and Korean astronomers selected smaller 'asterisms', or groupings of stars. Most older African civilisations identified individual stars, usually likening them to animals. For instance the bright star Betelgeuse was sometimes seen to represent a lion.

Some civilisations took particular note of the five visible planets. They appeared like bright stars, yet slowly wandered against the 'fixed' stars. The Babylonians likened them to gods, and believed that their movements influenced daily life on Earth. The obsession with celestial gods still continues today (see box on page 10).

Naming the days

Even the seven days of the week are named for those gods, day names already having been fixed and in use in Babylonian times. A curious system based on a recurring pattern underpins the naming of our days. By allocating the first hour of the first day to the slowest moving body – the planet Saturn – the week begins with Saturday. Subsequent hours are allocated respectively to Jupiter, Mars, the Sun, Venus, Mercury and the Moon, the sequence ranging from the slowest to the fastest moving. After seven hours, the cycle is repeated. After 24 hours, and more than three cycles, the first hour of the second day belongs to the Sun, hence Sunday. After further cycles of the seven heavenly bodies, the first hour of the third day falls under the Moon, hence Monday. Similarly the first hour of the fourth day belongs to Mars (Tuesday in English, but *Mardi* in French), that for the fifth day Mercury (*Mercredi* in French), for the sixth day Jupiter (*Jeudi*), and for the seventh day Venus (*Vendredi*), after which the cycle repeats.

Extraordinary events

While the progression of the planets against the fixed patterns of stars was a nightly performance, the occasional appearance of a comet was usually held in awe. Somehow, most ancient civilisations were quick to perceive them as bad omens – a resort to fatalism in everyday life. They could be believed to be the cause of natural disasters or even the excuse for war.

Eclipses of the Sun and Moon also struck fear. History records that a battle between the Medes and the Lydians in 585 BC was called off at the start of an eclipse of the Sun. However, the discovery of the 'saros' cycle in Asia and Europe allowed such events to be predicted. The astronomical term 'saros' refers to an interval of just more than 18 years after which the Earth, Sun and Moon return to nearly the same relative positions, and the cycle of lunar and solar eclipses begins to repeat itself.

Isilimela

Most of the people of ancient Africa grew crops for food. As agriculturalists, they needed a calendar to indicate when to prepare the fields and plant seed. The annual cycle of starry constellations (caused by the apparent motion of the Sun once around the sky in a year) presented them with a convenient calendar. Most constellations disappear from the night sky for a month or two while the Sun passes them. They reappear in the early morning sky, emerging from the eastern twilight. The reappearance of one particular pattern – a cluster of stars known as the 'digging stars', or Isilimela (in Xhosa) – signified the start of a new agricultural season. On its reappearance, fields were tilled, seeds planted and, when eventually the crops were harvested, Isilimela (the Pleiades cluster in Taurus) appropriately began to fade into the evening twilight in the west.

The reappearance of Isilimela is therefore the symbol of a new beginning. In Xhosa society it is also used as a time when initiation schools and ceremonies are carried out. Xhosa men count their years of manhood as so many 'Isilimelas', and the Xhosa name for the month of June (just as the stars reappear) is Isilimela. Other African people use other stars. Amongst them, the Swazi and northern Sotho look to the reappearance of Naka (Canopus) as the start of a new year. The first person to sight that star might be rewarded with a cow, and the ceremonial Mphaphala horn would be blown.

The lunar calendar

The cycle of the Moon's phases has provided a convenient short-term calendar. African people rejoiced in the reappearance of the crescent Moon in the early evening twilight; it was thought appropriate for business, or even wars, to be conducted around the time of Full Moon. Such activity traditionally declined as the Moon waned. The disappearance of the Moon close to New Moon was considered an inappropriate time for action. Both Africans and the early Romans named the months but allowed an extra month to be added in once every three years.

The Muslim calendar today is entirely lunar. Twelve cycles of the

Above African women toiling in the field.

Mons Mensae (Table Mountain)

Cape Town's Table Mountain is the only geographical feature on the Earth's surface to be represented as a constellation in the sky. The ancient Greeks never 'colonised' the portion of the southern sky that was not visible from Europe. Both Edmund Halley (of comet fame) and the French astronomer Louis de la Caille invented constellations to complete the Celestial Sphere, but it was those of the latter astronomer that were finally recognised. De la Caille was also a cleric and would have nothing to do with traditional mythological creatures, so instead he named constellations for scientific instruments and artists' equipment.

De la Caille carried out his work from the backyard of a house in Strand Street in Cape Town when he visited in 1751–52. So dominated was his view by the mountain, that he thought it was only right that one of the 14 constellations he named should be *Mons Mensae* (Latin for Table Mountain). The constellation of Table Mountain is hardly an impressive one: all its stars are very faint. But the abbé chose a patch of fuzzy, faint light in the sky, also known as the Large Magellanic Cloud, to represent the 'tablecloth', the cloud that forms on top of the mountain when the strong south-easter wind blows.

Right The icon of Table Mountain appears in the centre of this map, drawn by Abbé de la Caille in the 18th century.

Moon's phase, a total of 354 days, make up the Muslim year. By contrast, the Jewish year has, over a 19-year cycle, certain years with 12 true months, and certain years with 13, thus enabling the cycles of Sun and Moon to be run together.

Since the time of the ancient Egyptians, the agricultural or seasonal year has been the prime calendrical unit that underpins international calendars, even though it is 20 minutes shorter than the time it takes the Earth to orbit the Sun exactly once. In one such year, the Moon goes through 12,38 complete cycles of its phase. To accommodate both month and year, the Egyptians 'fudged' the months, to make exactly 12 fit into a year – which is how we manage today.

Establishing the starting point

The recent arrival of the new millennium highlighted some curiosities of our inheritance. The term 'Anno Domini' (AD) was invented in AD 525 by a Roman monk, Dionysius Exiguus. Although it was intended to

count years from the birth of Christ, the choice of the initial year was only an educated guess. It is now believed that Christ was born around 6–4 BC. Similarly, the start of the year was in March (hence September is the seventh month, and so on); the use of January 1 as the beginning of a new year reflects the start of a new financial year in the Roman Civil Service. So the designation of the year, and its starting point, are quite arbitrary.

Only in the last few hundred years – since Galileo turned a telescope to the heavens – have reasonable interpretations been made as to what we are actually seeing in the night sky. The planets have become worlds like our own. The stars are recognised as distant suns. The passage of the planets across the sky is simply a reflection of their orbiting around the Sun, as viewed from a planet that is itself also moving around the Sun. The patterns made by the stars are nothing more than our view of an almost random distribution in space; there is nothing mysterious about them. Nevertheless, we have retained the ancient naming of the constellations for convenience.

Herschel at the Cape

In the 18th and 19th centuries, a revolution was brought about in observational astronomy, thanks to the father and son combination of William and John Herschel. They perfected the construction of large reflecting telescopes (superior to anything else then available) and used them effectively to scan the heavens, discovering thousands of 'nebulae', hundreds of double stars, and numerous moons in our Solar System, including those of Uranus, the planet discovered by William Herschel in 1781.

John Herschel, 54 years the younger, followed his father in undertaking a complete survey of the heavens visible from England, not only verifying his father's discoveries, but adding to them. However, from England he could not see the southernmost portion of the sky, so in 1834–38 he relocated his telescopes to the Cape of Good Hope. There, beneath the eastern buttress of Table Mountain, he completed a telescopic survey of the entire sky – probably still the only man to have done so.

Sir John Herschel was, in his time, an eminent citizen of the Cape, who also contributed to the school system. The Grove Primary School is now situated in that part of Claremont where he lived. At its entrance, an obelisk commemorates the place where his great reflecting telescope stood, and various streets have been named in his honour. Aside from significant contributions to the field of astronomy, Herschel is also remembered for his philosophy, photography (a word coined by him), botany and chemistry – one of the world's great scholars.

Right Herschel's reflecting telescope is supported by the triangular trusswork. Behind it are Table Mountain and Devil's Peak. (Delineation by Sir John, using the camera lucida; details by GH Ford.)

CHAPTER 3

The universe on ever larger scales

In this chapter, we shall present a sequence of diagrams that illustrate the universe around us on an ever-increasing scale, from the size of the Earth (diagram 1) to the size of the entire visible universe (diagram 12). The diagrams are based on those displayed outside the Planetarium of the South African Museum in Cape Town.

The diagrams look very different from one another, yet each one has our position somewhere near the centre – with a reassuring 'You are here' indicator. One of the remarkable properties of the universe is just how different it looks when viewed at different scales. Some diagrams look busy, whereas others seem empty, except for isolated flecks of some sort. It says something of the universe that as one progresses through the sequence of diagrams, so the scene alternates between busy and quiet.

While this sequence carries one to the largest-known scale, one could also have a sequence that progresses to the smallest-known scale – through everyday life and down to the microscopic world, eventually to atoms and then atomic nuclei. The scenes would look very different – but would again alternate between busy and quiet: such is the nature of our universe.

The Earth DIAGRAM 1

We call our home 'Earth', although only a third of the surface of our planet is 'earth'; the rest is water. Perhaps 'Oceana' might have been a more appropriate name for our planet. But it is the 'earth' portion that is home to almost all mankind. It is hard to believe that we can find temperatures of about 1 000 °C within a hundred kilometres of our home – directly downwards towards the centre of the Earth. The centre itself is much hotter yet: it is thought to be about 6 600 °C, hotter than the surface of the Sun. The outward flow of heat from the Earth's interior causes the outer layers of the Earth, the mantle and the crust, to

move around in ultra-slow motion, at about the same speed as our fingernails grow. This motion, over many millions of years, shifts the continents – making them collide, merge, and later break apart. Consequently, the arrangement of continents that we see in this diagram is no more than a representation of how they are positioned at present.

San Francisco and the Bay area

Munich seen from space. In this false-colour radar image, built-up areas appear white, forests as pink, and agricultural terrain as green.

The Western Cape photographed from the space shuttle

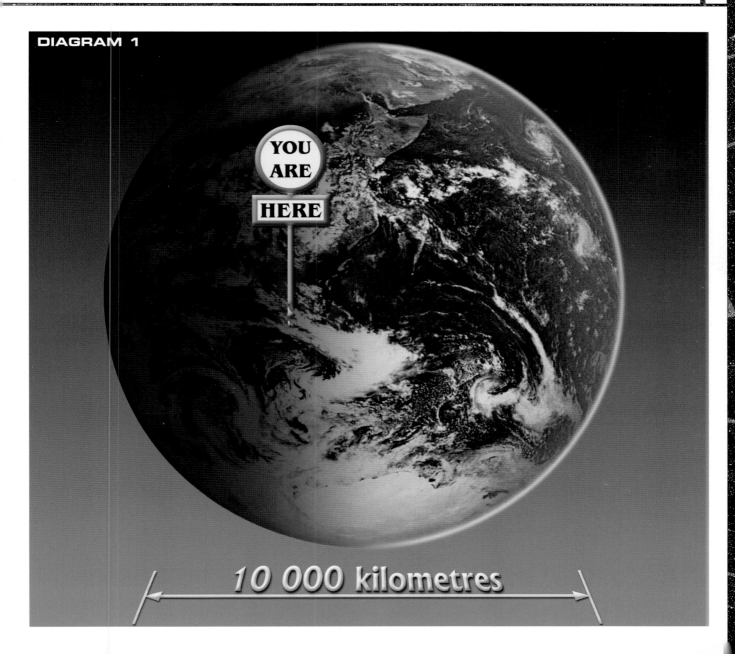

DIAGRAM 1

YOU ARE HERE

10 000 kilometres

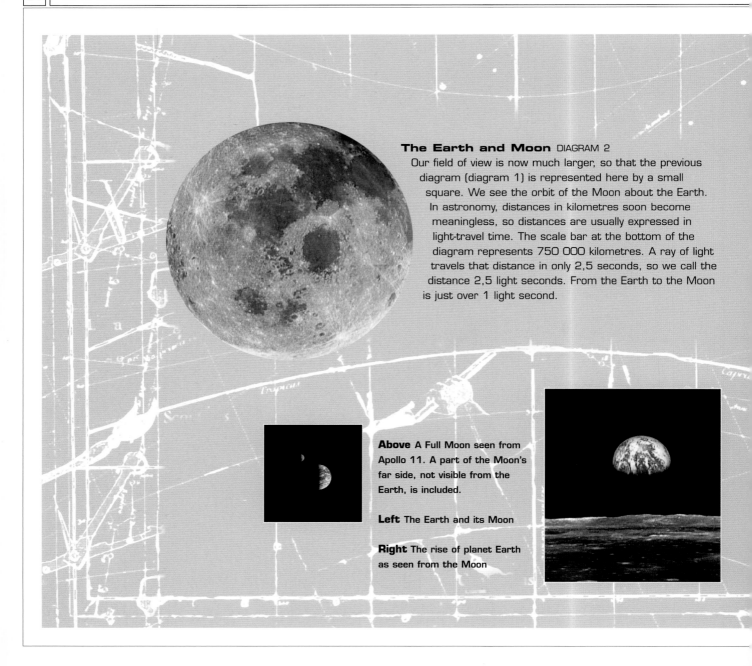

The Earth and Moon DIAGRAM 2

Our field of view is now much larger, so that the previous diagram (diagram 1) is represented here by a small square. We see the orbit of the Moon about the Earth. In astronomy, distances in kilometres soon become meaningless, so distances are usually expressed in light-travel time. The scale bar at the bottom of the diagram represents 750 000 kilometres. A ray of light travels that distance in only 2,5 seconds, so we call the distance 2,5 light seconds. From the Earth to the Moon is just over 1 light second.

Above A Full Moon seen from Apollo 11. A part of the Moon's far side, not visible from the Earth, is included.

Left The Earth and its Moon

Right The rise of planet Earth as seen from the Moon

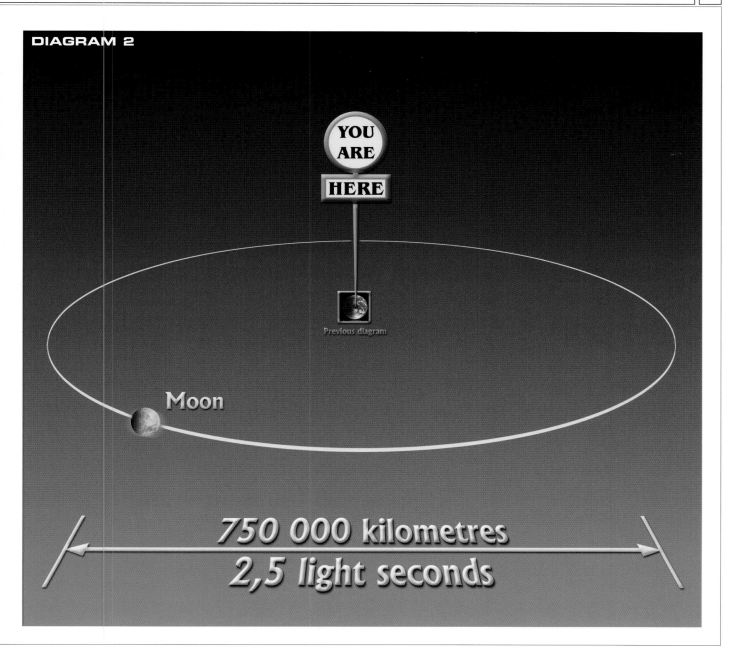

DIAGRAM 2

YOU ARE HERE

Previous diagram

Moon

750 000 kilometres
2,5 light seconds

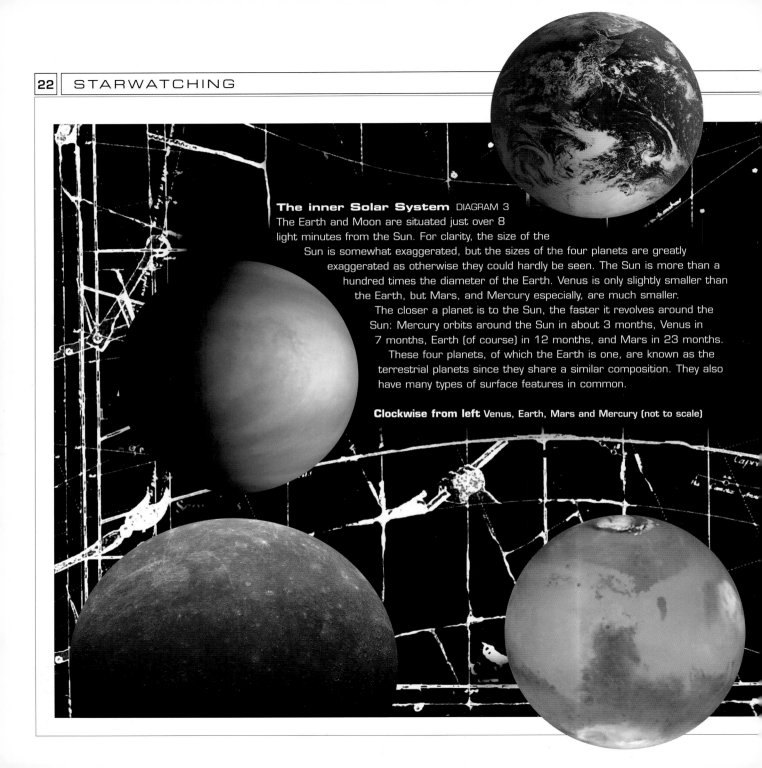

The inner Solar System DIAGRAM 3

The Earth and Moon are situated just over 8 light minutes from the Sun. For clarity, the size of the Sun is somewhat exaggerated, but the sizes of the four planets are greatly exaggerated as otherwise they could hardly be seen. The Sun is more than a hundred times the diameter of the Earth. Venus is only slightly smaller than the Earth, but Mars, and Mercury especially, are much smaller.

The closer a planet is to the Sun, the faster it revolves around the Sun: Mercury orbits around the Sun in about 3 months, Venus in 7 months, Earth (of course) in 12 months, and Mars in 23 months. These four planets, of which the Earth is one, are known as the terrestrial planets since they share a similar composition. They also have many types of surface features in common.

Clockwise from left Venus, Earth, Mars and Mercury (not to scale)

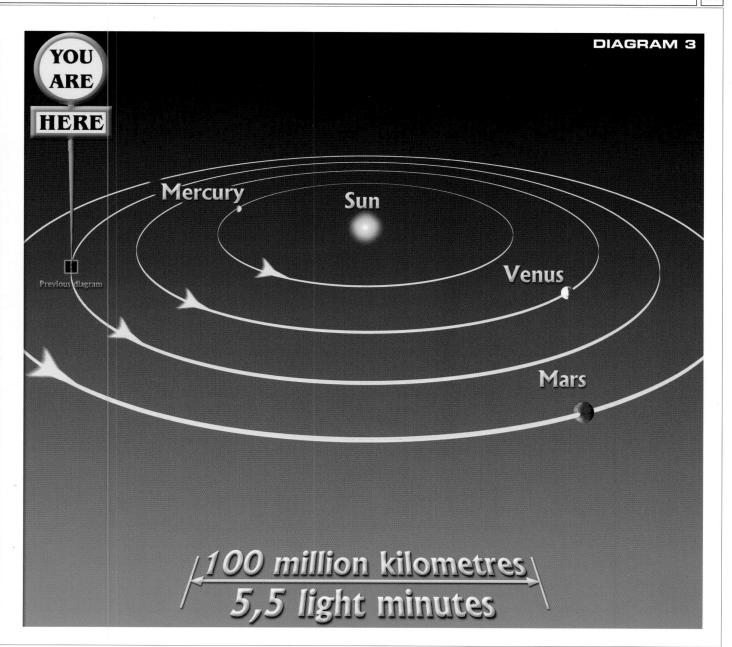

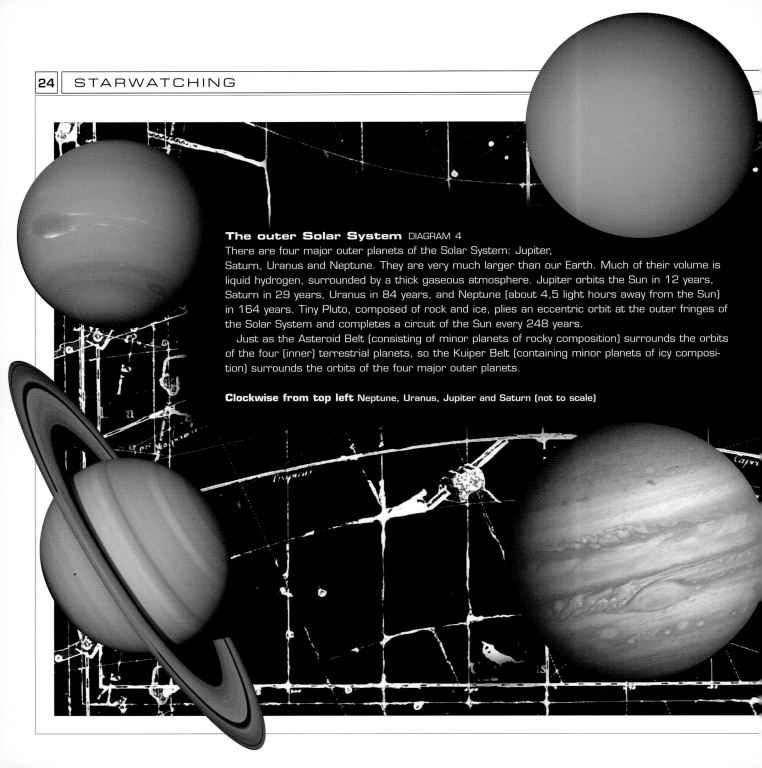

The outer Solar System DIAGRAM 4

There are four major outer planets of the Solar System: Jupiter, Saturn, Uranus and Neptune. They are very much larger than our Earth. Much of their volume is liquid hydrogen, surrounded by a thick gaseous atmosphere. Jupiter orbits the Sun in 12 years, Saturn in 29 years, Uranus in 84 years, and Neptune (about 4,5 light hours away from the Sun) in 164 years. Tiny Pluto, composed of rock and ice, plies an eccentric orbit at the outer fringes of the Solar System and completes a circuit of the Sun every 248 years.

Just as the Asteroid Belt (consisting of minor planets of rocky composition) surrounds the orbits of the four (inner) terrestrial planets, so the Kuiper Belt (containing minor planets of icy composition) surrounds the orbits of the four major outer planets.

Clockwise from top left Neptune, Uranus, Jupiter and Saturn (not to scale)

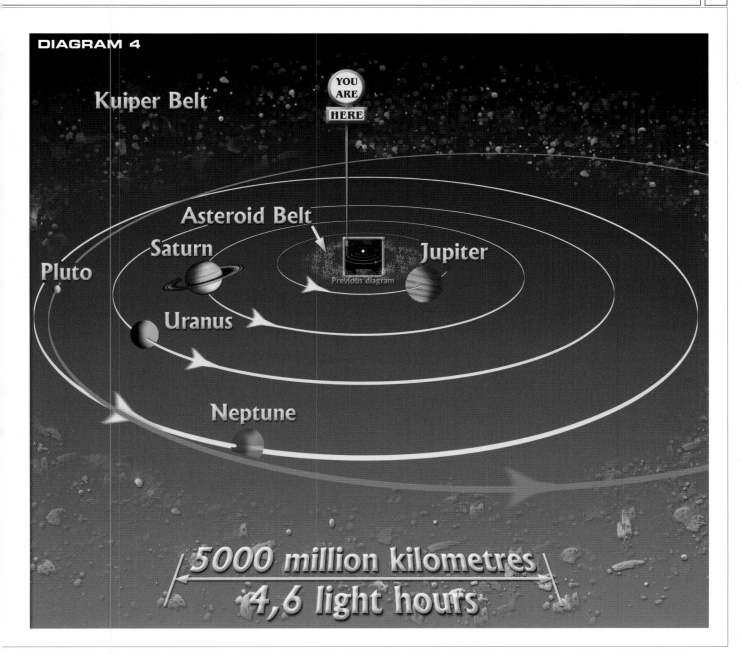

The sun is a star DIAGRAM 5

A halo of tiny icy bodies – the Oort Cloud – apparently surrounds our Solar System. If one of these bodies falls in close to the Sun, it forms the seed of a gigantic, yet tenuous, cloud of water vapour, which is seen from Earth as a comet.

As the scale is enlarged still further, our Sun – the familiar disc seen from Earth – has shrunk to a pinpoint. The Sun now appears for what it is – just another star, isolated in the vastness of space.

Stars are very much larger than planets and the gravitational energy released during their formation has raised their central temperatures to millions of degrees – high enough for nuclear reactions to be initiated. It is these nuclear reactions that provide the energy that keeps the stars shining. Even the surface temperatures reach thousands of degrees, so obviously stars are gaseous throughout. The vast reservoir of heat and energy created by the nuclear reactions in their cores leaks slowly through the outer layers to be radiated off into space. The survival of life on Earth is not just dependent on the Earth's composition, but also on its being at the right distance from a star like our Sun.

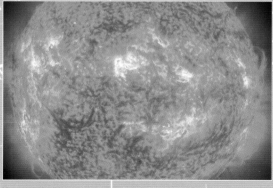

Stars like our Sun are gaseous throughout.

Comet Hale-Bopp

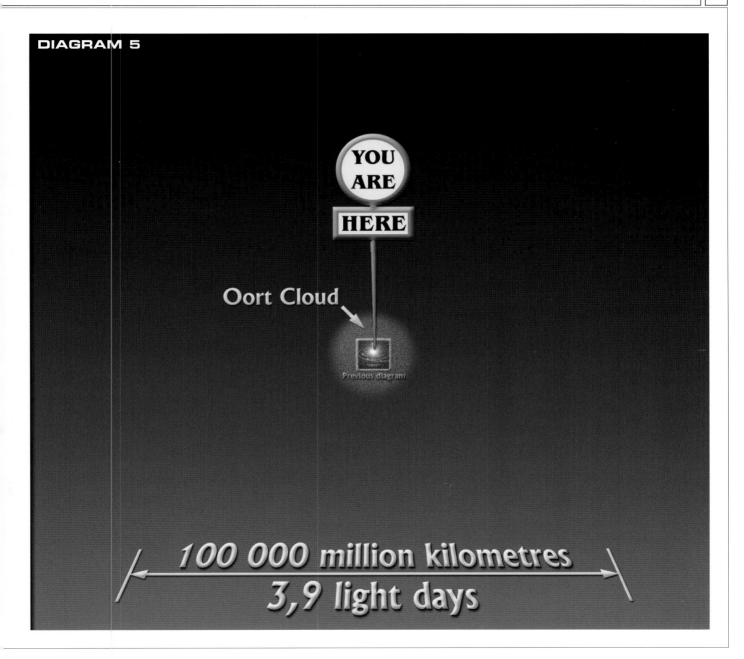

DIAGRAM 5

YOU ARE HERE

Oort Cloud

Previous diagram

100 000 million kilometres
3,9 light days

The nearest stellar neighbour DIAGRAM 6

In this illustration, our nearest neighbouring solar system is revealed. Whereas the distance to the outer planets in our Solar System is over four light hours, here we see that the distance to the Alpha Centauri system is over four light years! When we look at Alpha Centauri in the night sky – we see it as one of the 'Pointer' stars to the Southern Cross – it appears as it used to be over four years ago, and not as it is at the moment.

Our Solar System has a single star – our Sun – but this neighbouring system has three suns. The two brightest suns orbit about one another in 80 years; a third very faint star (Alpha Centauri C) lies far away from the other two, but is thought to orbit very slowly about them.

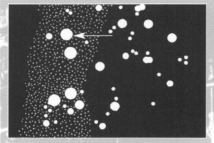

Alpha Centauri appears in the sky as one of the 'Pointer' stars next to the Southern Cross. To the eye, it appears as a single bright star, whereas a telescope reveals its separate components.

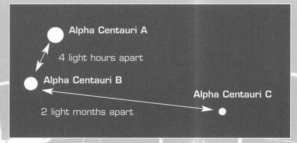

The Alpha Centauri system consists of three suns. Alpha Centauri C, the closest to our Solar System, is also known as Proxima Centauri.

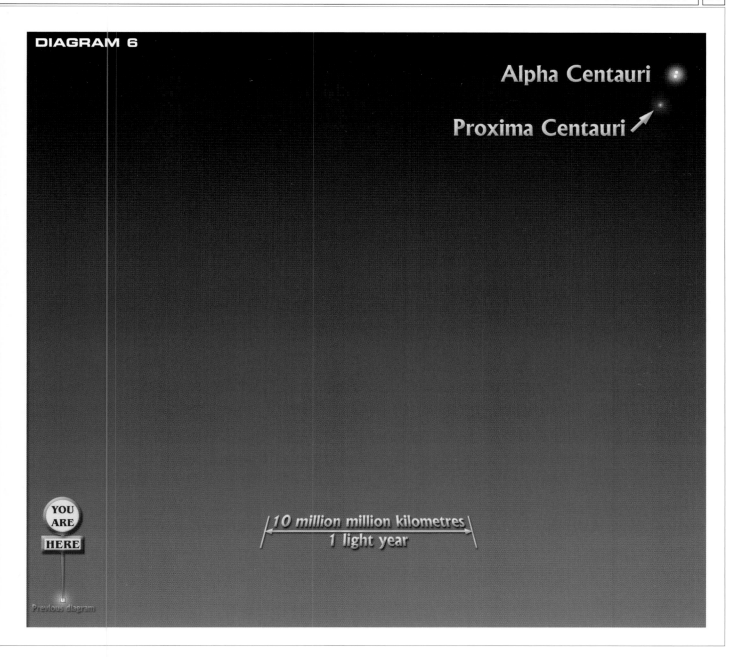

DIAGRAM 6

Alpha Centauri

Proxima Centauri

10 million million kilometres
1 light year

YOU ARE HERE

The solar neighbourhood DIAGRAM 7

In our 'solar neighbourhood', stars are scattered at a few light years' distance from one another. Many, like Alpha Centauri, are double or triple systems. Most stars are thought to possess systems of planets – though these planets would be almost impossible to see from Earth. Some of the stars are even brighter than our Sun, but most are very much dimmer. Those labelled in this diagram are amongst the brightest stars seen in our night sky.

Since the distance from Earth to each of these stars would be measured in terms of light years, we see them in the night sky as they used to be many years ago, and not as they are at the moment. For instance, Sirius is seen as it was 9 years ago, Procyon 11 years ago, Altair 16 years ago, and Vega 26 years ago. Aldebaran, the most luminous star here, is seen as it was almost 70 years ago.

Top Sirius (left) and Procyon (right), in the constellations of Canis Major and Canis Minor, are two of the closest neighbours to our Solar System.

Centre Altair, in the constellation of Aquila, is a nearby star.

Below left Vega, in Lyra, is relatively nearby.

Below right Pollux and Castor, in Gemini, are not particularly distant.

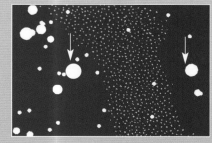

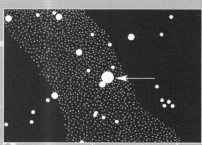

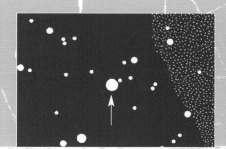

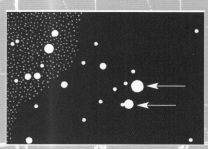

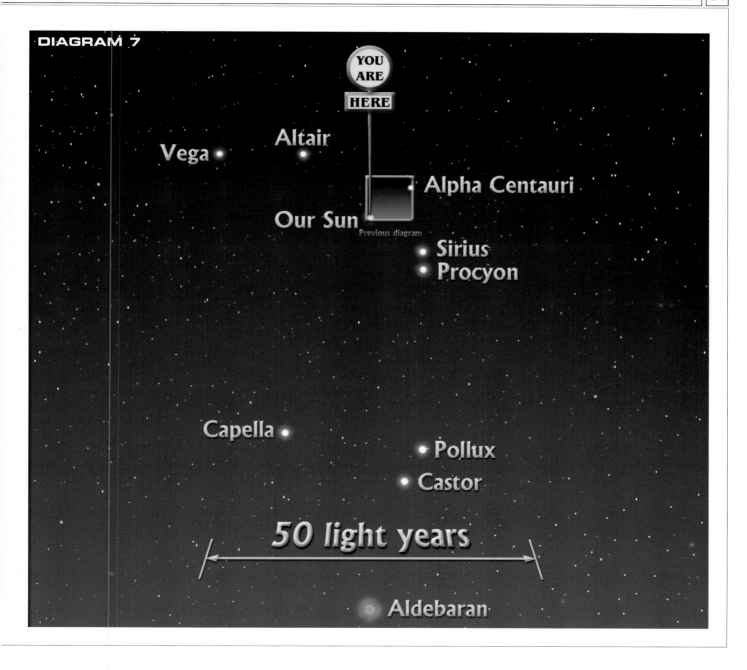

DIAGRAM 7

YOU ARE HERE

Vega

Altair

Alpha Centauri

Our Sun
Previous diagram

Sirius
Procyon

Capella

Pollux

Castor

50 light years

Aldebaran

Our local portion of the Galaxy DIAGRAM 8

In this diagram, with a scale extending over thousands of light years, the light of countless millions of stars is merged. Some stars are much more luminous than our Sun – even hundreds or thousands of times more luminous! A few of them are amongst the brightest stars in our night sky (though they are much more distant from us than the stars in the solar neighbourhood). These very luminous stars are concentrated in a band across the middle of the diagram – known as the Orion Arm, named after the dense concentration of hot young stars, gas and dust of the Orion Association. Condensations of interstellar dust, including the Great Rift, form opaque clouds and lanes, especially along the upper edge of the Orion Arm. The regularity of the structure is disturbed by the concentration of the Eta Carina region.

This distribution of stars is flattened towards the plane of the paper. Seen from the Earth, it forms the encircling band of the Milky Way.

Above right Stars, at various stages in their life cycles, are captured in this view of a galactic cluster.

Right Stars, luminous gas and dark dust clouds in the Eta Carina region

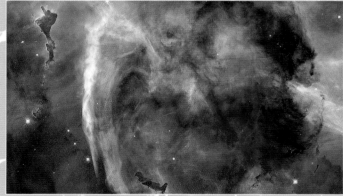

DIAGRAM 8

Eta Carina

YOU ARE HERE

Great Rift

Previous diagram

Orion Association

5 000 light years

Our Galaxy DIAGRAM 9

Everything we have seen so far is part of an immense stellar system – our Galaxy. Altogether there are about a million million stars in the Galaxy; many are packed in the central bulge. Surrounding the bulge is a disc of stars, gas and dust. The most luminous stars (and gas) in the disc make a conspicuous spiral pattern. The Orion Arm, which we encountered in the previous diagram, is believed to be a 'spur' more than a major spiral arm. Closer to the centre is the Sagittarius Spiral Arm (named for the foreground constellation), and further from the centre is the Perseus Spiral Arm. Our Sun and its Solar System are situated about 30 thousand light years from the centre of the Galaxy.

When observing the night sky, and looking in the direction of the constellations of Scorpius and Sagittarius, we are, in fact, looking towards the centre of the Galaxy. Of course, what we see as the centre of the Galaxy is what it was like 30 thousand years ago, and not as it really is at the moment.

Just as the planets in our Solar System orbit around the Sun, so the Sun and stars in the disc orbit around the centre of the Galaxy – but one revolution takes about 200 million years!

An infrared view of the sky penetrates much of the dust clouds of the
Milky Way and reveals our entire Galaxy stretching around us. The
centre of the Galaxy is obvious.
A panorama of the Milky Way (our Galaxy) seen from within, is shown
later in this book on pages 68 and 69.

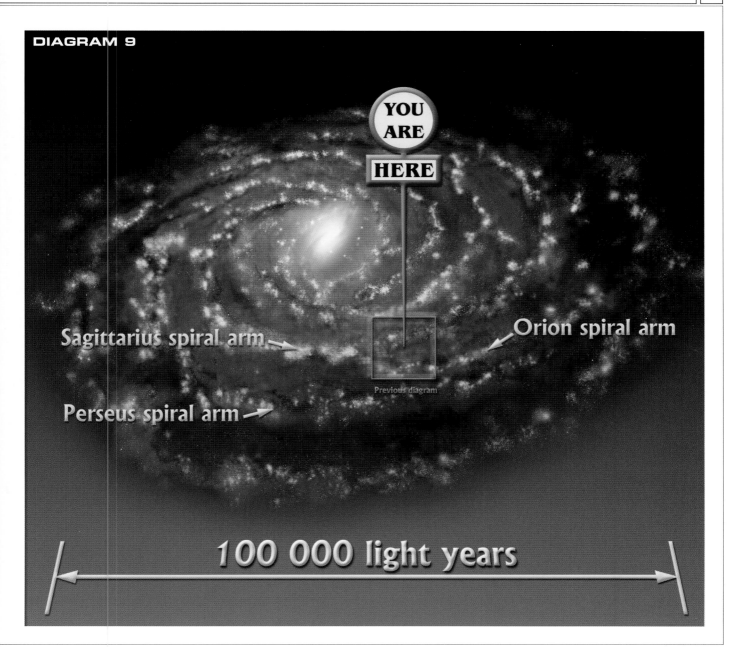

DIAGRAM 9

YOU ARE HERE

Sagittarius spiral arm

Perseus spiral arm

Orion spiral arm

Previous diagram

100 000 light years

The Local Group of galaxies DIAGRAM 10

Until the 1920s, most astronomers thought the Galaxy comprised the entire universe. Today, we know that our Galaxy is not unique – and that there are billions of other galaxies!

The nearest neighbouring minor galaxies are the Magellanic Clouds – about 170 thousand light years away and visible as diffuse patches in our southern sky. The nearest neighbouring major galaxy is the Great Galaxy in Andromeda (Messier 31) – about 2 million light years distant. Thus we see this galaxy in our night sky as it was 2 million years ago. The two big galaxies – the Milky Way and Andromeda – with a sprinkling of lesser galaxies around them, form the 'Local Group'.

The Great Galaxy in (the constellation of) Andromeda, with its two small companion galaxies. The stars scattered over the entire view are foreground stars in our Galaxy; the stars in the Andromeda galaxy are too distant to be seen individually.

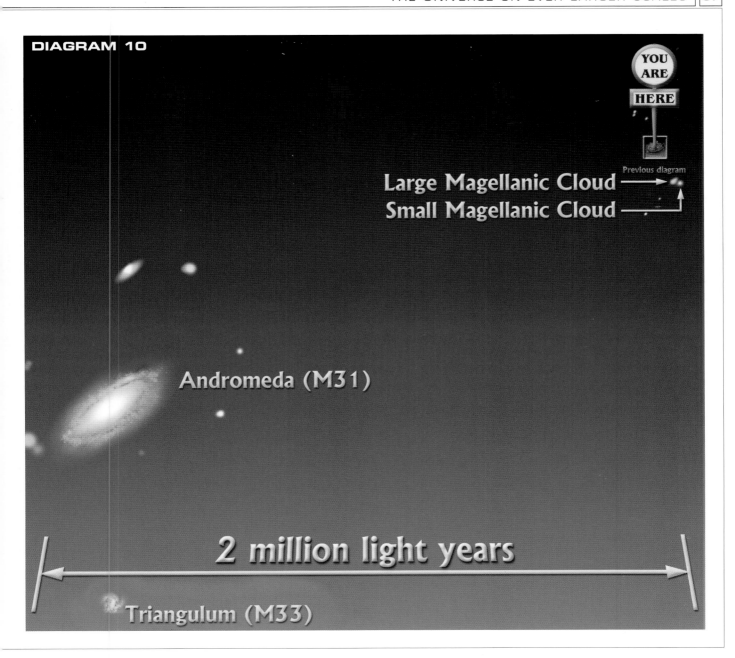

DIAGRAM 10

YOU ARE HERE

Previous diagram

Large Magellanic Cloud →
Small Magellanic Cloud →

Andromeda (M31)

2 million light years

Triangulum (M33)

Neighbouring superclusters DIAGRAM 11

This diagram indicates the distribution of the major groups of galaxies. Our Local Group lies on the fringe of the 'Virgo Supercluster', an irregular concentration centred on the Virgo Cluster, about 50 million light years away. The Virgo Supercluster is in turn an appendage of the gigantic Centaurus Supercluster. On a still larger scale, a great labyrinth of interconnected superclusters is revealed. Many of the concentrations form great wall-like structures, some running in almost straight lines for a billion light years! There is a tendency for the walls to intersect each other at right angles. Between the concentrations are almost empty spaces – the voids in this great cosmic texture.

The cosmic texture is growing ever larger as the universe expands. In general, the spaces between the galaxies are growing larger – though the galaxies themselves, and even the groups and clusters, do not grow larger. As a result, we see the Virgo Cluster moving away from our Galaxy (Local Group) at 1 000 kilometres a second. The more distant the clusters or superclusters, the faster they recede from us: the Centaurus Cluster is moving away from us at 3 000 kilometres a second, whereas the Coma Cluster is moving away at over 6 000 kilometres a second!

Again, by looking further out, we are forced to look back in time. The Coma Cluster is seen as it was 350 million years ago, and not as it is at the moment.

Top and middle The Perseus Cluster of galaxies and the Coma Cluster of galaxies

Right The objects labelled are galaxies in the nearby Virgo Cluster. The other objects are foreground stars in our Galaxy.

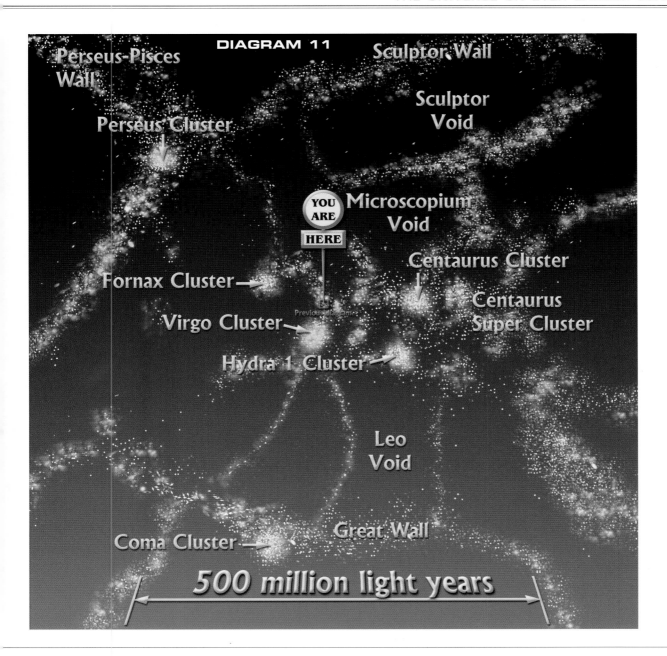

DIAGRAM 11

Perseus-Pisces Wall

Sculptor Wall

Perseus Cluster

Sculptor Void

YOU ARE HERE

Microscopium Void

Centaurus Cluster

Fornax Cluster

Centaurus Super Cluster

Virgo Cluster

Hydra 1 Cluster

Leo Void

Great Wall

Coma Cluster

500 million light years

The Entire Observable Universe DIAGRAM 12

Modern cosmological theory indicates that the universe began in an explosive 'big bang' that continues today, in the form of the expansion of the universe. The rate of expansion that we observe today indicates that the beginning was around 15 billion years ago. Consequently, the furthest we can ever see – the limit of the observable universe – is 15 billion light years. The diagram suggests this limit as a spherical horizon – it is the horizon for us, although this is not to say we are in the centre of the universe, nor do we know if the universe is finite or infinite beyond that horizon.

As we look further outward, we have to look further back in time, though the images we see become very distorted and stretched out. We cannot see to the very beginning, since the very early universe (the first half million years) was very hot and opaque (just like the inside of our Sun). We can look back to the time when that incandescent universe became transparent. The light then emitted has survived, although it is now stretched to microwaves. The Cosmic Microwave Background that we observe today is a grossly stretched-out image of the early universe, seen over the entire sky. It shows the early universe to be remarkably smooth and uniform. However, the COBE satellite, launched in 1989, discovered some very small fluctuations. Those fluctuations, although amounting to only one part in 100 000, are believed nevertheless to have seeded the formation of superclusters and galaxies, from whence came the stars and planets, even our own Sun and our own planet.

Since the very early universe was opaque (before the light that is now the Cosmic Microwave Background was emitted), we appear to be enclosed within an opaque spherical shell – a 'Cosmic Egg'. It is not a physical structure, as it exists in time, not in place. We cannot see through the shell, nor can we see any further out into the universe or further back in time.

Starting at home, with the Earth and Moon, we have now had an overview of the universe and its constituents, on ever-larger scales. The next six chapters follow a similar route, giving detailed information and insight.

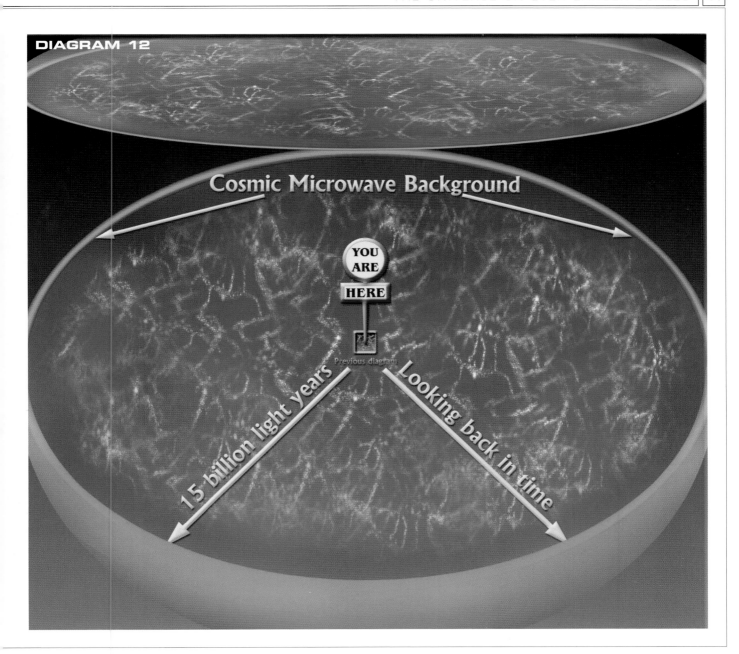

DIAGRAM 12

Cosmic Microwave Background

YOU ARE HERE

Previous diagram

15 billion light years

Looking back in time

CHAPTER 4

The Moon

In our Solar System, no other planet as small as the Earth has a natural satellite as large as the Moon. Our Moon is thought to have originated when a body about half the diameter of Earth collided with our home planet shortly after the Solar System was formed, some four and a half billion years ago. The Moon is a remnant of that collision. It is only a quarter the diameter of the Earth and an eightieth of its mass.

Originally the Moon was much closer to the Earth than it is today. At this proximity, the Earth would have subjected it to extreme tidal forces, flexing its crust as it spun. Eventually this tidal drag is calculated to have stopped the spin of the Moon relative to the Earth, resulting in the situation as it is today, with one face of the Moon permanently turned towards the Earth, the other side permanently turned away.

The Moon is now doing the same to the Earth, slowing its spin, but the process is even more protracted than Earth's stopping the Moon. A day and night on Earth was originally much shorter – probably lasting only a few hours. In the distant future, a day and night will be 40 times as long as present – at which point the Earth will be locked to the Moon, turning only one face to its satellite. In this process, the Moon will have moved much further from the Earth.

A surface pummelled by impacts

Over the eons of time of its existence, the Moon – like all other bodies in our Solar System – has been pummelled by impacts, particularly as the 'left-overs' from the formation of the Solar System were swept up. Unlike the Earth, whose land masses are constantly sculpted by the forces of water, erosion has been almost absent on the surface of the Moon. So dense are the impact craters on the Moon that older impacts are largely obliterated by more recent impacts.

The Moon's near side, in particular, exhibits enormous impact craters that are hundreds of kilometres across, and made almost four billion years ago. These craters so fractured the crust that molten lava from the Moon's then hot interior flowed out, and in a series of floods (possibly spanning a few million years) filled up the crater interiors. The filled craters are known as maria, and form the well-known dark patches on the Moon (they occur on Mercury and Mars as well). Erroneously believed to be 'seas' on the Moon, the maria basins have attracted fanciful labels such as the Sea of Tranquillity (or *Mare Tranquillitatis*, to give it its official Latin name). Craters on the Moon have generally been named for famous scientists and philosophers. The map opposite identifies the most conspicuous craters and maria on the near side of the Moon. Though the lava surfaces are obviously smoother than the lighter coloured regions – and were where the Apollo lunar landers touched down – they have nevertheless been peppered with numerous impacts since their formation.

The cratered texture of the Moon's surface makes it an interesting object to view through a small telescope. The craters are most obvious close to the lunar terminator – the boundary between night and day on the Moon – where the low Sun casts dramatic shadows. To the naked eye the Moon looks like a silver globe. In reality, the eye exaggerates the amount of light; it should appear dull grey, reflecting only about 6% of incident light.

Almost the entire surface of the Moon is covered by a layer of loose, powdery soil resembling dry cement powder – hence the dull grey colour. This layer has been created over billions of years as small meteor bodies have pummelled the surface. Scattered too on the surface are rocks, the debris of somewhat larger impacts. Embedded in the lunar soil are microscopic glass beads – debris thrown up from massive impacts (melted matter that then solidified as it fell back and was scattered on the Moon's surface). These beads function as a back-scatterer of light, much like the plastic beads that coat car number plates, to reflect light back towards its source. As a consequence of this, the Moon brightens around Full Moon when the Earth is positioned to receive the back-scattered light. The effect is most prominent in the rays radiating from young craters where the beads are still relatively young. Over a

MOON MAP

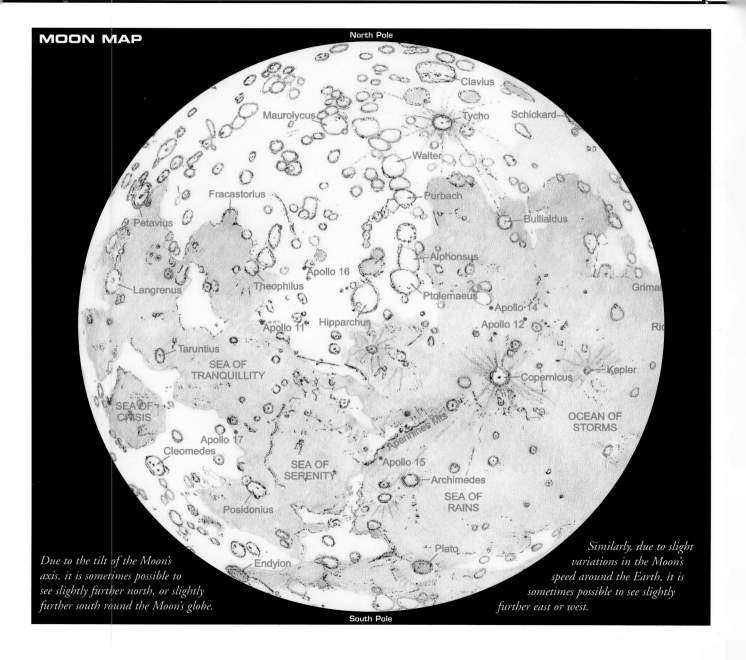

North Pole

Clavius

Maurolycus

Tycho

Schickard

Walter

Fracastorius

Purbach

Petavius

Bullialdus

Alphonsus

Apollo 16

Langrenus

Theophilus

Ptolemaeus

Grimal

Apollo 14

Hipparchus

Apollo 12

Ric

Apollo 11

Taruntius

SEA OF
TRANQUILLITY

Copernicus

Kepler

SEA OF
CRISIS

OCEAN OF
STORMS

Apollo 17

Apennines Mts

Cleomedes

Apollo 15

SEA OF
SERENITY

Archimedes

SEA OF
RAINS

Posidonius

Plato

Endylion

South Pole

Due to the tilt of the Moon's axis, it is sometimes possible to see slightly further north, or slightly further south round the Moon's globe.

Similarly, due to slight variations in the Moon's speed around the Earth, it is sometimes possible to see slightly further east or west.

period of millions or billions of years, however, exposure to particles in the 'solar wind' causes microscopic pits in the beads that rob them of their reflective power. Similarly, the constant pitting of the surface by tiny meteors softens the sharp contours of impact craters. Geologists can therefore give an approximate age to any lunar feature; and since younger features overlap or obliterate older features, establishing relative chronology is possible.

Orbits within orbits

The Moon circles the Earth once in 27,3 days. Because the Earth is at the same time orbiting the Sun, the time from New Moon to New Moon is 29,5 days. On account of a 5° tilt to its axis and a slightly eccentric orbit, the visible face of the Moon appears to nod slowly up and down and left and right; in all, 59% of its surface is at some time visible from Earth. The eccentric orbit means that the Moon is sometimes slightly closer to, or further from, the Earth. The point when it is closest is known as Perigee; its distance is then about 360 000 kilometres from Earth. The furthest point is known as Apogee, at a distance of 400 000 kilometres.

Although the gravitational pull of the Moon on the Earth is not as great as that of the Sun, its proximity causes it to have a tidal effect about three times as strong as that of the Sun. This tidal pull stretches the Earth, the oceans responding more willingly than the solid crust. Twice during the Moon's 29,5-day revolution – at New Moon and at Full Moon – it aligns its tidal force with that of the Sun, producing 'spring tides'. At First and Last Quarter, the Sun and Moon work against each other, resulting in the milder 'neap tides'. Tides are also intensified when the Moon is close to Perigee. When Perigee and spring tides coincide – as they do twice a year – extreme tides are experienced.

The Moon is, of course, the furthest destination reached by the human race (see box opposite). As well as performing a range of complex tasks, the Apollo missions successfully brought back extensive geological samples. They also confirmed that the Moon was devoid of life.

Dreams remain of establishing a permanent lunar base, and it is only a matter of time before humans again walk on its surface. The far side of the Moon is shielded from radio radiation from Earth, making it an ideal post from which to listen to the radio waves from the rest of the universe.

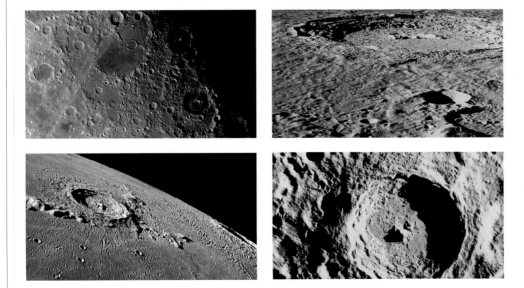

Top left *Craters on the Moon are seen best close to the lunar terminator – the boundary between day and night on the Moon.*

Top right *The crater Copernicus (at top) seen from a spacecraft orbiting the Moon*

Far left *The crater Eratosthenes*

Left *The crater Tycho*

The Apollo Landings

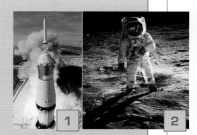

It is disappointing that more than 30 years have now passed since man was on the Moon. The Apollo landings took place just 11 years after the United States successfully launched its first satellite into space, and eight years after President John Kennedy stated it as the aim of the United States Space programme. Kennedy's announcement had triggered a new requirement: spacecraft would have to be able to rendezvous with each other in orbit and dock with one another. The original Mercury spacecraft that carried a single astronaut was inadequate for the task. To develop the necessary skills, project Gemini – involving a more manoeuvrable, two-man craft in near-Earth orbit – was launched.

Another key to the success of the Moon flights was the gigantic Saturn rocket, still the heaviest vehicle ever to lift off the ground. At take-off, it weighed some 3 600 tonnes and burnt 11 tonnes of fuel per second. Werner von Braun, who perfected the German V2 rocket during the Second World War, was largely responsible for its design. In fact, the first of three stages of the Saturn rocket burnt out at similar altitude as its V2 predecessor. Second and third stages carried it up to orbit around the Earth, and the third stage then fired again to hurtle the Apollo vehicles towards the Moon. After this, the command module separated from the third stage, turned around, then docked with the lander module and plucked it from its rocket housing. Once close enough to the Moon, the command module's motor was used to brake the combined spacecraft so that it entered into orbit around the Moon.

Two of the three astronauts then entered the lander module, detached it from the command module, and used its rocket engine first to leave orbit, and then to brake as it fell to a soft landing on the Moon. Once down, the astronauts donned spacesuits to roam in the vicinity of the spacecraft, in some cases extending their range by means of a 'lunar rover'. Only the upper stage of the lunar lander returned to orbit, to carry the astronauts back to the command module, the only section of the original spacecraft to return to Earth.

A series of manned lunar missions followed, two in preparation for landing. Apollos 11, 12, 14, 15, 16 and 17 made successful landings. The Apollo 13 mission was aborted when an oxygen tank exploded.

Years later it became known that the Soviet Union had also been racing for the Moon, developing lunar landers similar to the Americans. However, the Soviet Moon Rocket – the equivalent of the Saturn 5 – twice blew up on test flights, and the Americans claimed victory before the Soviet's problems could be overcome.

Right top to bottom 1. Apollo 11 spacecaft, atop the mighty Saturn rocket, at lift off; **2.** Astronaut Aldrin on the surface of the Moon; **3.** Astronauts set up experiments on the lunar surface; **4.** The crew of Apollo 11, the first to land on the Moon: Neil Armstrong, Michael Collins and Edwin Aldrin; **5.** The Apollo 11 capsule is recovered from the sea.

When seen from the Moon, the Earth also shows phases.

Phases and visibility

Like the Earth, the Moon is illuminated by sunlight. Only half the Moon can be lit up at a time (its day-time side), while the other side is in darkness (its night-time side). The Moon revolves around the Earth in 29,5 days (relative to the Sun). Consequently, there is a time when we see only its sunlit side (at Full Moon) and a time when it turns only its dark side towards us (at New Moon). In-between, we may see half the sunlit side and half the dark side (First Quarter and Last Quarter). The Moon shows a crescent phase when we look mainly on its dark side, and see only a slither of the sunlit side. It also shows a gibbous phase, when we see mainly the sunlit side.

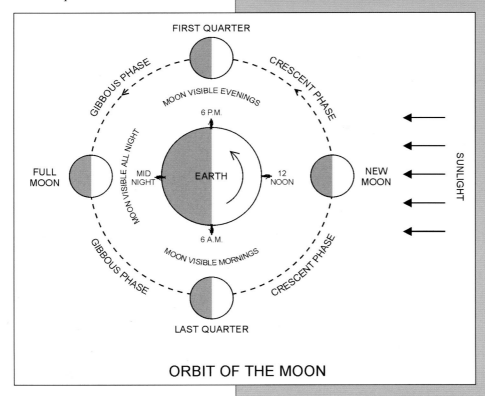

ORBIT OF THE MOON

The accompanying diagram shows the 29,5-day cycle of the Moon's phases. It includes a representation of the Earth, looking down on the North Pole; from this aspect, the Earth rotates anti-clockwise in 24 hours (midday, 6 p.m., midnight and 6 a.m. are marked). From the diagram, we can see that at New Moon, the Moon is entirely in our daytime sky (and impossible to sight, unless it passes directly in front of the Sun – see box opposite). At First Quarter, the Moon is visible in the afternoon and evening. At Full Moon, it is visible all night (coming up when the Sun goes down, and going down when the Sun comes up). At Last Quarter, it is visible in the early morning hours and the morning.

Eclipses of the Moon

The Earth casts a long conical shadow, more than a million kilometres long, into space. Our diurnal passage through this shadow as the Earth rotates is, of course, the reason for our night time. Because the Moon's orbit around the Earth is slightly tilted to the plane of the Earth's orbit around the Sun, the Moon usually manages to miss this shadow when it is on the opposite side of the Earth to the Sun (i.e. at Full Moon). However, twice a year, the nodes (the intersection of the two planes) lie close to the Full Moon position, and the Moon may consequently pass through the Earth's shadow.

A total eclipse of the Moon occurs when the Moon passes completely into the Earth's shadow. Typically, it will take about an hour to enter the shadow completely, anything up to an hour in 'totality' and about an hour to re-emerge. During the 'partial' phase – going in or coming out of the shadow – the Moon presents an odd appearance as the Earth's shadow (circular and much larger than the Moon) cuts across its disc. At totality, the Moon does not completely disappear, as some light refracted through the Earth's atmosphere gives it a reddish hue.

Partial eclipses, when the Moon is partially but not totally eclipsed by Earth's shadow, sometimes occur. 'Penumbral' eclipses refer to the Moon's passing through the outer 'penumbral' shadow of the Earth (and not the full 'umbral' shadow), but they are not normally apparent to the human eye.

Eclipses occur only at Full Moon and can be seen from the night-time hemisphere of Earth. Consequently, half of our planet (the side in darkness) has the opportunity for witnessing any particular eclipse of the Moon.

ECLIPSE OF THE MOON

MOON · EARTH · SUNLIGHT · Earth's shadow

Moon – basic data
Diameter: 3 480 km (27% of Earth)
Mass: $7,35 \times 10^{22}$ kg (1/81 of Earth)
Surface gravity: 0,16 Earth
Average distance from Earth: 384 000 km
Closest distance (Perigee): Approx 357 000 km
Furthest distance (Apogee): Approx 407 000 km

CHAPTER 5

Planets, moons and smaller bodies of our Solar System

The inner Solar System comprises the four terrestrial planets – Mercury, Venus, Earth and Mars – surrounded by the 'Asteroid Belt' of minor planets. Beyond this lies the outer Solar System's four giant planets – Jupiter, Saturn, Uranus and Neptune – surrounded by the Kuiper Belt of minor planets (the largest of which is Pluto).

The terrestrial planets, our Moon and the 'asteroids', are similar in composition, being either rocky or having a rocky mantle surrounding an iron-nickel core. They also show many common surface features – impact craters, volcanoes, lava plains, canyons and valleys, for instance. Impact cratering is ubiquitous throughout the Solar System, but erosive forces on the Earth, Venus and Mars have, to varying degrees, obliterated the older craters.

The heavy elements of the giant planets are probably confined to their relatively small cores, their bulk being largely made up of low-density liquid hydrogen, surrounded by outer gaseous layers.

Of the terrestrial planets, only the Earth has a proper moon; Mars has two tiny captured asteroids as moons. By contrast, each of the giant outer planets possesses many moons, each like a miniature Solar System in itself. Some of these moons are the size of planets, Ganymede (in Jupiter's system) and Titan (in Saturn's system) being larger than planet Mercury. Added to these regular moons are numerous tiny minor planets (apparent from their irregular orbits) captured by the major planets. Though the major moons have rocky cores, their dominant composition is water ice. Smaller moons are probably wholly water ice – albeit somewhat dirty ice.

The numerous minor planets of the Kuiper Belt, which is situated just beyond the orbit of the last giant planet, Neptune, are similarly thought to be composed mainly of water ice.

Mercury

Mercury is the smallest of the eight main planets of the solar system (but much larger than Pluto). Pictures of Mercury are easily mistaken for our Moon; it is peppered with craters and also possesses large 'maria' basins. But there are differences; closer inspection reveals some spaces between the craters (whereas the Moon's surface is cratered everywhere). Also, internally, it possesses a large iron-nickel core (as deduced from its magnetic field), whereas the Moon does not.

Perhaps one of the strangest things about Mercury is that a day and night on the planet would last for two Mercurian years (or six of our calendar months). Adding to the complication is the planet's fairly eccentric orbit: its distance from the Sun varies sufficiently to cause the radiation received by the planet to be twice as intense at some times of year as at others. Two points on opposite sides of Mercury's equator are 'hot spots': whenever they experience noon, Mercury is closest to the Sun. Midway between them, also on the equator, are two relatively cool spots where noon always occurs when Mercury is furthest from the Sun.

Right *Mercury*

Venus

Although it is said to be Earth's 'sister' planet, Venus sports a very hostile environment, an outcome of its dense, thick atmosphere of carbon dioxide. That atmosphere creates an extreme 'greenhouse' effect, trapping so much heat that the average surface temperature on Venus is around 500°C. The atmosphere is so dense that landing a spacecraft on Venus would be somewhat like lowering a bathysphere (submersible observation chamber) deep into the Earth's ocean – and subject to some 90 times the atmospheric pressure.

The soaring temperature rules out liquid water, although Venus has continent-sized highlands, elevated well above the extensive lowlands. Aside from a few large impact basins, Venus shows plenty of evidence of volcanic activity, particularly in a band stretching along its equatorial region. Such mapping has been achieved by radar (especially from the Magellan spacecraft), since dense white clouds in its thick atmosphere make it impossible to sight the surface in normal light – or for any stars to be sighted from its surface.

Curiously, Venus is a slow rotator, a day and night taking 127 of our days to pass. However, winds in the upper atmosphere appear to carry cloud patterns around the planet in only four of our days.

Earth

The surface features of the land masses of Earth are, of course, well known to its inhabitants. But the crust beneath the ocean is remarkably thin and mobile, causing the continents to move around constantly, and to collide and break apart. This happens in ultra-slow motion (at about the same speed as our fingernails grow). None of the other inner (terrestrial planets) shows such activity. Furthermore, because the land masses are constantly showered with rain and so eroded by the deposited water, barely an impact crater remains intact.

The rain has also washed away most of the atmosphere – carbon dioxide dissolves in rain water and ends up in the sea or in limestone rock. The abundance of liquid water, which results from the planet's being neither too close to, nor too far from, the Sun, has led to the emergence of life on Earth. Yet for most of its history, that life has been microscopic and confined to the oceans. Only in the past 10% or so of the planet's existence have macroscopic life forms developed and colonised the land. Of the millions of different species of plants and animals that have evolved in this recent history, one species – *Homo sapiens* – has had a major impact on the planet's vegetation and environment, with potentially devastating consequences.

Mars

Very much smaller than the Earth, and most closely resembling it in our Solar System, Mars is aptly described as the 'desert' planet, its surface sporting fields of sand dunes and barren rocky outcrops. With its relatively lower surface gravity, some of its features exceed their terrestrial counterparts in size. It possesses a network of canyons (rift valleys) – called Valles Marinus – that are far larger and deeper (up to 6 kilometres deep) than any terrestrial counterpart. It has a conical volcano – Montes Olympus – three times the height of Mount Everest, and some 500 kilometres across at its base.

In many ways it also resembles the Moon, as about 60% of its surface is peppered with craters, including

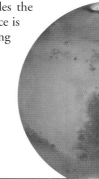

Top left Venus

Top right Almost half of Earth is covered by cloud.

Right Mars

the gigantic Hellas basin. The craters are nowhere as densely packed as those on the Moon, as erosion has evidently greatly reduced their numbers.

The planet's atmosphere – largely composed of carbon dioxide gas – is very thin, with less than 1% of the Earth's atmospheric pressure.

Nevertheless, the possibility that Mars might support life has long excited human interest. Following the apparent sighting (by Schiaparelli in 1877) of a network of straight lines – the infamous, and non-existent, canals – speculation was rife about Martian civilisations. However, the visit of the Viking spacecraft in 1976 presented evidence that strongly suggested the planet was sterile. Interest was revived by a claim made in 1996 that micro-fossils (nowhere near the size of bacteria) were present in a Martian meteorite, but the evidence has subsequently been discredited. Nevertheless, a new wave of exploration has shown that there are reservoirs of water – the essential ingredient of life – underground.

The reason for the almost smooth northern portion of the planet has been a mystery. A possible explanation is that it was once the bed of a shallow ocean. Some evidence for ancient sea shores has been put forward; other evidence points to there having been substantial water flows in the past. If so, the climate must then have been much warmer.

Mars possesses two tiny moons, undoubtedly captured asteroids. Phobos has an irregular shape, is about 30 km long, and orbits in seven hours. Deimos, somewhat smaller, orbits once in 30 hours. Despite their size, both moons are peppered with impact craters.

The Asteroid Belt and meteors

Vast numbers of minor planetary bodies are gathered in a belt between Mars and Jupiter. It is not clear whether a major planet once existed in that orbit, and which might subsequently have broken up – or whether the multitude of asteroid bodies has been there since the Solar System was formed.

The few asteroids that have been photographed close-up reveal cratered surfaces. Most are fairly low density. Some even have companions – tiny moons – orbiting about them.

Collisions might be the cause of some asteroids and smaller pieces losing orbital speed and falling in closer to the Sun. Inevitably, they eventually collide with one of the inner planets. The Earth in particular suffers frequent impacts by asteroidal material. Smaller fragments, which are incinerated in the Earth's upper atmosphere, are seen from the Earth as 'meteors' or 'shooting stars'.

Occasionally, larger meteors make it to the ground and are recovered as 'meteorites'. The majority of meteorites are rocky in nature and difficult to identify once landed. Perhaps 15%, however, are iron meteorites and distinct in appearance, such as those outside the planetarium in Cape Town.

Jupiter and moons

Jupiter (left) is the innermost of the giant planets and the biggest planet in the Solar System. It is some 11 times the Earth's diameter and 300 times more massive. In character, it is very different from the terrestrial planets, being largely liquid hydrogen, with a small core of heavier elements. Its outermost layer is gaseous.

Phobos

From top Jupiter's
moons: Io, Callisto,
Ganymede and
Europa (not to scale)

Cloud formations within that outer layer give the planet a dramatic appearance. In general, they form bands parallel to the planet's equator, the lighter being clouds that are pushed up by rising gas underneath. The darker the bands, the deeper into the atmosphere our line of sight penetrates. The bands show slow variations in time. Superimposed on the bands are a variety of spots – effectively cyclonic storms. Many are transient, but the famous 'Great Red Spot' has persisted as long as telescopic observations have been carried out.

Jupiter is effectively a star that didn't make it. Had it had more mass, nuclear fusion would have been triggered in its core. Nevertheless, in forming, it generated a great deal of heat inside, and still radiates much more heat than it receives from the Sun. The planet is also visibly flattened by its rapid rotation; in spite of its gigantic size, the planet completes a rotation in less than ten hours.

Jupiter possesses a well-developed system of moons, as though it constituted a small Solar System in itself. While many of its 50 or more moons are small, and almost certainly captured asteroids, there are four very large moons, including Ganymede (which is larger than the planet Mercury). The innermost moon, Io, is stressed and heated by Jupiter's tidal effect, causing it to be extremely volcanic. Heat from Jupiter affects the second moon, Europa, less, but is still sufficient to melt its outer, otherwise icy, layer. It now appears to have a thin icy crust covering what is presumably an ocean, making it the only other 'water planet' like our Earth in the Solar System. The other two large moons, Ganymede and Callisto, appear to have mantles of water ice around a rocky core.

Close to Jupiter, coinciding with its equatorial plane, is a flattened ring, apparently consisting of fine, dull debris.

Saturn and moons

Saturn (left) is best known for its prominent ring system. The rings consist of thousands of ringlets, each a swarm of gleaming icy nuggets. Incredibly, though the system is more than 300 000 kilometres in diameter, it is probably less than 100 metres thick. By the laws of physics, ringlets closer to Saturn must rotate faster than those further out. That, and the fact that occasionally stars have been seen through the rings, proves that they are not solid.

Saturn is a somewhat smaller version of Jupiter. Its atmosphere shows a band structure and spots similar to that of Jupiter. Unlike Jupiter, there is a yellowish haze above the

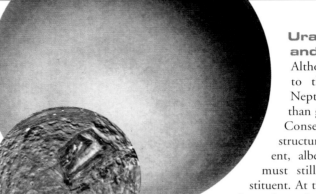

clouds, giving the planet a distinct yellow colour. The internal structure must resemble that of Jupiter, although the outer gaseous layer is much deeper.

Saturn too has a great system of moons. The largest is Titan, big enough to possess an atmosphere, and with a surface hidden by clouds. All the others exhibit cratered surfaces, even though their surfaces and interiors are little more than dirty ice.

Uranus, Neptune and moons

Although massive compared to the Earth, Uranus and Neptune are much smaller than giants Jupiter and Saturn. Consequently, their internal structures must be quite different, albeit that liquid hydrogen must still be a significant constituent. At times both planets present almost featureless discs, Uranus a greenish colour and Neptune blue. At other times, dark spots and white (high altitude) cloud is present.

Both planets have a multitude of moons, the majority of which, when photographed close-up, reveal cratered surfaces. However, one of Uranus's moons, Miranda, displays a surface fragmented into segments of very different terrain – aptly described as 'a moon designed by a committee'.

Triton, the largest of Neptune's moons, shows no craters but displays a strange crenellated surface. Astonishingly, given the extremely low prevailing temperature, erupting geysers are apparent – possibly of liquid nitrogen.

Both planets have ring systems – but more discrete rings rather than the extensive system of Saturn.

From top Saturn's moons: Tethys, Titan, Dione and Enceladus (not to scale)

Top of page Uranus and Miranda (in front)

Left to right Triton, Oberon and Titania (not to scale)

Pluto and the Kuiper Belt

Although once thought to be a major planet of the Solar System, Pluto is not nearly as large as our Moon. Nor is it unique in its orbital position: there are plenty of other minor planets outside the orbit of Neptune, constituting the Kuiper Belt. Pluto is obviously an icy world, but it has yet to be examined close up with the help of a spacecraft. We know however that it has a moon, Charon.

Comets and the Oort Cloud

We can be confident that there are no major planets beyond the Kuiper Belt, but occasional comets fall in from even further out, implying the existence of a great reservoir of small icy bodies surrounding the Solar System in a halo known as the Oort Cloud.

Comets themselves are 'dirty icebergs'. The nucleus of Comet Halley is about the size of Table Mountain. Comets fall inwards, towards and often into the Sun, but more usually in long parabolic orbits that carry them close to the Sun. As they are heated, so the ice sublimates (turns into water vapour), so that a gigantic, but very tenuous, cloud of water vapour – the visible comet – surrounds the tiny nucleus. Influenced by the Sun's ultra-violet light, much of the cloud becomes ionised and is then carried outwards by the 'solar wind' to form a bluish tail. Similarly, the dirt in the iceberg produces dust, blown outwards by solar radiation to form a yellowish tail.

Many comets do not survive, but occasionally a comet is slowed by Jupiter and goes into a smaller orbit, such as that of Halley, which returns to sweep past the Sun every 75 years, until hardly anything is left. Jupiter has also been known to capture a comet: Comet Shoemaker-Levy 9 eventually broke up and crashed into the planet in 1994. Other comets 'burn out', leaving a trail of debris in orbit. When the Earth encounters such debris, a meteor shower results.

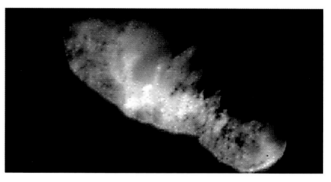

Top *Pluto and its moon, Charon*

Middle *The nucleus of Comet Borelly*

Right *Comet Kohoutek*

Planets seen with the naked eye

Five planets of our Solar System – Mercury, Venus, Mars, Jupiter and Saturn – are clearly visible to the naked eye. The planets are too far away for the eye to discern any size, so they resemble bright stars. Unlike stars, planets do not twinkle, but shine with a fairly steady light.

The name 'planet' implies a wanderer, for unlike the 'fixed' stars, they are seen – over weeks or months – to wander against the starry background. A 'planetarium' is basically a device for portraying the complex wanderings of the planets.

Venus is usually the third brightest object in the sky, after the Sun and Moon. Quite often, it is bright enough to be clearly visible in the daytime, though spotting it is a challenge. Since it lies closer to the Sun than the Earth, it is seen either in the western sky after sunset, or in the eastern sky before sunrise (over a 19-month cycle).

Jupiter is also extremely bright, but not quite bright enough to be seen in daylight. Since it takes about 12 years to orbit the Sun – and therefore to appear to go once around the Celestial Sphere – it wanders only very slowly from one constellation to the next.

Mars can vary greatly in luminosity, according to its distance from the Earth. Every 25 months, the Earth approaches, overtakes it, and leaves it behind. During such a time, Mars appears very bright and also traces a loop or zigzag path against the starry background. Mars has a distinct reddish colour that makes its identification easy.

Neither Mercury nor Saturn appear as bright as the other three. Being very close to the Sun, Mercury appears either just after sunset in the western twilight or just before sunrise in the eastern twilight. Saturn has something of a yellowish colour and is the slowest moving of the 'big five'.

Planets - basic data

	DISTANCE FROM SUN IN MILLION KM	PERIOD OF REVOLUTION IN YEARS	MASS COMPARED TO EARTH	DIAMETER COMPARED TO EARTH	PERIOD OF ROTATION	TILT OF EQUATOR TO ORBIT (DEG)
Mercury	58	0,24	0,05	0,39	59 d	0
Venus	108	0,62	0,82	0,95	243 d	178
Earth	150	1,00	1,00	1,00	23 h 56 m	23,5
Mars	228	1,88	0,11	0,53	24 h 37 m	24
Jupiter	778	11,90	319,00	11,20	9 h 51 m	3
Saturn	1 426	29,50	95,00	9,40	10 h 14 m	27
Uranus	2 868	84,00	15,00	4,10	17,2 h	98
Neptune	4 494	164,80	17,00	3,80	17,8 h	30
Pluto	5 896	247,60	0,002	0,15	6,4 d	118?

Planets seen through a telescope

Planets can usually be seen as tiny discs when viewed through a modest telescope. The accompanying illustration indicates the relative sizes and degree of detail visible.

Venus reveals no surface features as it is permanently enshrouded in white cloud. However, because we look upon its 'night' side as it approaches and overtakes the Earth, it shows phases similar to those of our Moon.

Jupiter also has a relatively large disc. With good viewing conditions (when Earth's atmosphere is stable), dark equatorial bands and its Great Red Spot (when turned towards us) are visible. As their orbits are seen almost edge on, the four main moons of Jupiter form a line passing through Jupiter. Their configurations change from night to night. Occasionally they are seen to pass in front of, and then slip behind, the planet.

The disc of Saturn is generally too small for any detail to be seen, but its ring system makes it a great favourite. Over the cycle of its 29-year orbit, the rings change their tilt relative to the Earth.

Mars and Mercury show only tiny discs, and it is difficult to discern features, other than by using larger telescopes in excellent observing conditions.

Uranus and Neptune require special finding charts, being below naked-eye visibility. In good conditions, they can just be discerned as planets.

Pluto can only be seen through a large telescope and in appearance is indistinguishable from a star.

The appearance of the planets and their larger moons as seen by a visually experienced observer, using a moderately sized telescope

Mercury

Venus

Mars

Jupiter

Saturn

Uranus

Neptune

Pluto

CHAPTER 6

Our star, the Sun

Whereas the Sun appears as a blazing incandescent disc against a blue daytime sky, the stars are twinkling points of light in the blackness of the night. Given this discrepancy in what we see, it is hard to realise that the Sun is simply the nearest star – and that the night-time stars are distant suns. Even the nearest star is more than 250 000 times more distant than the Sun; hence the enormous difference in appearance and the equally enormous difference in apparent brightness. The Sun outshines the brightest stars we see by 10 000 million times.

Moreover, the Sun is the centre of our Solar System, an oasis of light in the blackness of space, in and around which the planets and minor bodies bask. The Sun is far larger and far more massive than its planets. In comparison with the Earth, the Sun is over 100 times greater in diameter, over 1 000 000 times greater in volume and over 300 000 times greater in mass. It is this vast superiority in mass that promoted it to 'stardom', when it became a hot, incandescent sphere that gives off light, rather than a cool planet that does not emit visible light.

A flaming ball of gas

The Sun is sufficiently hot to be gaseous throughout. Although it seems to present an outer surface, that surface (known as the photosphere) is no more than the place where the gas changes from being opaque to becoming transparent. Although that surface is extremely hot by everyday standards, it is tepid in comparison to that of the interior. The temperature just a short distance below the surface is over 1 000 000°C. The temperature in the very centre of the Sun is calculated to be some 15 000 000°C.

In the same way as the temperature varies, so does the mass density. At the surface, the gas is much less dense than the air we breathe, yet in the centre, the gas is three or four times more dense than lead.

Under such extreme temperatures and pressures, nuclear fusion takes place. In the core of the Sun, hydrogen is being fused to make helium. Yet, for every 4 kg of hydrogen processed, only 3,97 kg of helium are made. The small amount of mass lost is directly converted to energy (as described in Einstein's famous $E = mc^2$). It is this energy that keeps the Sun shining – and our Earth habitable.

There is enough heat bottled up inside the Sun to allow for a couple of million years' coasting without energy production. However, there is enough hydrogen in the Sun's core to fuel the nuclear reactions for some 10 000 million years. Our Sun is about halfway through its life. Like all stars, it must have been formed from the collapse, under gravity, of material in interstellar clouds. In the process, it inherited the products of earlier generations of stars, along with their small percentage of heavy elements. The composition of the Sun, by mass, is about 70% hydrogen, about 28% helium and about 2% heavier elements.

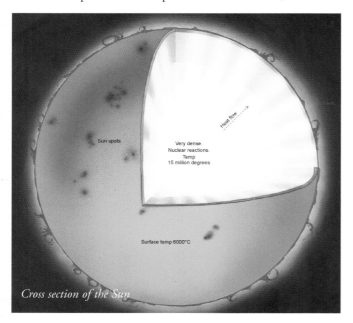

Sun spots

Very dense.
Nuclear reactions.
Temp
15 million degrees

Heat flow

Surface temp 6000°C

Cross section of the Sun

Sunspots

The Sun rotates about its axis, but not as a solid body. Its equatorial region goes around once in about 25 days, its polar regions in about 30 days. The difference causes the magnetic field within the Sun to be stretched, contorted and tangled. In places, loops of tightly twisted magnetic field break through the surface of the Sun. At the points of entry and exit of these concentrated magnetic loops, darker regions appear, indicating a disruption of the flow of heat from the solar interior. These darker regions are known as 'sunspots'. In reality, they have a temperature of about 4 000°C, and appear dark only in comparison to the surrounding surface which glows at about 6 000°C.

Rapid variations and changes in sunspot regions may result in enormous amounts of energy being transported by the magnetic fields. In certain cases, this may give rise to flares, which last only minutes. Above the disturbed region, great arcs of gas may flow and move within the magnetic lines, not unlike the flames of a gigantic fire. Quite often the magnetic field lines become open-ended and stretch off into space, so a jet of material streams outward into space. In general, the magnetic activity pumps energy into the very tenuous atmosphere that surrounds the Sun, known as the corona, causing its temperature to soar to millions of degrees Celsius. Under such conditions the corona is continuously boiling away, streaming radially outwards from the Sun to form the 'solar wind'. However, the amount of gas actually involved and the mass loss to the Sun is negligible.

Sunspot activity on the Sun peaks every 11 years; in between, the Sun is relatively quiescent. A new 'cycle' of sunspots first shows itself in disturbances around 40° north and south of the Sun's Equator. As the sunspot activity increases, so the bands of disturbance migrate towards the Equator, eventually fizzling out at about 5° from the Equator. Magnetic lines of force of the double sunspots show a common polarity within the same hemisphere – and an opposite polarity in the opposite hemisphere. The polarity also switches from one sunspot cycle to the next.

Years 2000 and 2001 marked a peak in solar activity. Many of the sunspots were large enough to be visible to the naked eye (which should be shielded by metallic shades to reduce the intensity of sunlight). Ejected material was seen to strike the magnetosphere that surrounds the Earth and give rise to prominent auroral displays.

The Sun will not last forever in its present form. As its fuel reservoir declines, it will swell outward sufficiently to bring an end to life on Earth. Our planet may even be vaporised. Fortunately, such a fate is still some five billion years in the future. A more detailed account of how the lives of stars end follows in the next chapter.

Above right The disc of the Sun in visible light reveals scattered sunspots.

Far right An X-ray photograph of the Sun accentuates the active regions. It also reveals the corona, the extended very hot, yet tenuous, gas that surrounds the Sun.

Right Detail of a coronal loop seen in X-rays.

The movement of the Sun across the daytime sky

Everyone knows that the Sun rises in the east and sets in the west. However, it is only at the equinoxes (approximately March 21 and September 23) that it rises exactly east and sets exactly west. During the winter months (from the perspective of the southern hemisphere), it rises north of east and sets north of west. In summer, it rises south of east and sets south of west. The Sun is at its highest (above north on the horizon) midway between rising and setting. However, as the accompanying diagram shows, in midwinter the Sun never reaches a great height above the horizon, while in midsummer it passes high overhead.

When the Sun is high in the sky and its rays strike the ground almost perpendicularly, its heating effect is greatest. When the Sun is low in the sky, its rays strike the ground obliquely and its heating effect is diminished. Consequently, its greatest heating effect is around midday, and not early morning or late afternoon. Similarly, its heating effect is far greater in summer, when it passes almost overhead, than in winter, when it never rises high in the sky.

Sun – basic data
Diameter: 1 392 000 km
(109 times the Earth)
Mass: $1,99 \times 10^{30}$ kg
(330 000 times the Earth)

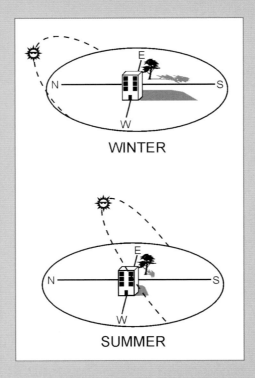

WINTER

SUMMER

Eclipses of the Sun

While the Moon can on occasions be completely immersed in the shadow of the Earth (see Eclipses of the Moon on page 47), the reverse is not possible. The Moon has only a quarter of the Earth's diameter, so its shadow can never cover the Earth. What is more, the Moon's shadow tapers in a cone shape, the point of which may only just touch the Earth's surface. It is only on relatively rare occasions that the tip of the Moon's shadow falls on the Earth's surface, making a small dark spot, usually about 150 kilometres across. From within that spot, the Moon is seen to cover the Sun completely, in a total eclipse of the Sun. As the Moon orbits the Earth, so the spot sweeps across the Earth's disc in a matter of two or three hours. The dark spot therefore travels at thousands of kilometres an hour across the Earth. Fortunately, such eclipses can be forecast with great precision, years in advance, so observers can be positioned along the track, ready to experience, typically, three or four minutes of totality as the spot passes over them. Unfortunately, the weather along the eclipse track cannot be forecast with similar certainty. In August 1999, many thousand of observers in Cornwall, England, were disappointed when clouds ruined their eclipse viewing.

A total eclipse of the Sun is, however, one of the most spectacular sights nature provides. With the bright disc of the Sun completely obscured, the elegant and tenuous corona around the Sun is visible. Where there are active regions near the outer edge of the Sun's disc, red prominences may be visible to the naked eye, often accompanied by long radial streamers. The surrounding sky is relatively dark – dark enough for bright stars to be seen in what should be daytime.

Before and after totality, the partial phases are visible. It takes the Moon about an hour to move over the Sun, and another hour to leave it. Similarly, observers not within the eclipse track may witness a partial eclipse. During this time, care has to be exercised in looking at the Sun, as sustained viewing may damage the retina of the human eye. Special spectacles with metallic foil, which reflects almost all the light, heat and ultra-violet rays, must be worn for safe viewing.

On occasions, when the Moon is at, or approaching, its greatest distance from the Earth, and when it passes directly between the Sun and the Earth, its conical shadow just fails to reach the Earth's surface. In this case, no total eclipse can be seen. Instead, an annular eclipse (from *annulus*, a ring) is seen, with the Moon not quite large enough to cover the Sun's disc.

Total eclipses typically occur about once every 18 to 24 months, somewhere on the Earth's surface. South Africa experienced a total eclipse of the Sun in October 1940 – the track cutting from the west coast across to East London. There was an annular eclipse in 1963 through Cape Town and two 'near misses' in 1992 and 1994, with tracks some 400 kilometres off the southwestern Cape. On June 21, 2001, a total eclipse track cut across Angola, Zambia, northeastern Zimbabwe and Mozambique. On December 4, 2002, a similar track cuts across Africa on the border between Zimbabwe and South Africa, though the duration of totality is not much longer than a minute.

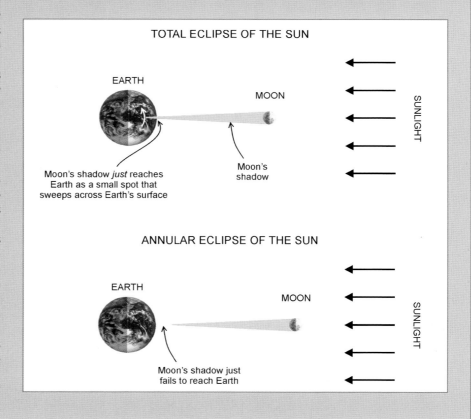

TOTAL ECLIPSE OF THE SUN

EARTH

MOON

SUNLIGHT

Moon's shadow *just* reaches Earth as a small spot that sweeps across Earth's surface

Moon's shadow

ANNULAR ECLIPSE OF THE SUN

EARTH

MOON

SUNLIGHT

Moon's shadow just fails to reach Earth

CHAPTER 7

Other stars

We see them as mere pinpoints of light, but every star is a sun more or less like our own. It is only their enormous distance that makes them appear so tiny. Up close, each star is a huge, incandescent sphere. Many of the stars you see in the night sky are bigger and brighter than our Sun, though our Sun (somewhat reassuringly) is brighter than average. Nevertheless, there are stars up to a million times brighter than our Sun, and stars almost a million times fainter. There are stars several hundred times the diameter of our Sun and stars only a hundredth of its diameter (the latter would be about the size of the Earth, but vastly more dense).

Like the Sun, stars give off abundant light because they generate energy by nuclear fusion in their cores. Some stars – if

not the vast majority – have planets orbiting around them, which bathe in their host star's light.

Less likely to have planets are close double stars (two suns in orbit about one another), which is a very common occurrence. Most of our neighbouring systems are widely spaced doubles. Multiple systems of up to six suns have been identified.

Star nurseries

Like raindrops that condense in a cloud, stars condense within interstellar clouds composed of gas and dust. Shock waves (from the spiral structure in a galaxy or from supernova explosions) probably initiate the process. After that, gravity takes over, the condensations growing as more and more material is drawn into them. Eventually an interstellar cloud may be transformed into a cluster of stars. The timescale for the formation of a star is far too slow to witness in the space of a human lifetime. But in the same way that a walk in a forest might reveal young saplings and mature trees together, our observations of space have allowed us to identify stars at various stages of formation and maturity. In support of the finding that interstellar clouds are star nurseries, newly formed embryonic stars have been found within interstellar clouds, such as the well-known Great Nebula in Orion.

As gravity shrinks the proto-star, so its matter is formed into a spherical shape. It gets hotter from the release of gravitational energy. If the core becomes sufficiently hot, nuclear reactions start, and the body becomes a star. Our own sun obviously succeeded in this regard, but calculations suggest that a body having less than 7% of the Sun's mass would not attain high enough temperatures to achieve sustained nuclear fusion. The

Erosion by the winds from hot young stars has sculpted these pillars from interstellar matter. Within the pillars, dense condensations will probably contract further to form new stars.

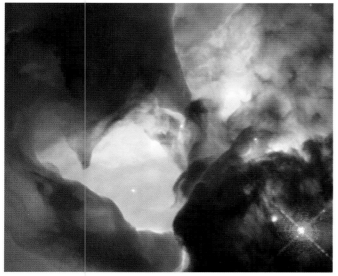

Top left *The Great Nebula ('Great Cloud') in Orion is effectively a 'maternity home' where new stars are born. Much of the gas glows after being excited by radiation from a group of central stars.*

Top right *Light from an embedded star reflects on a surrounding dust cloud.*

Left *The heart of the Lagoon Nebula shows remarkable structures caused by hot young stars.*

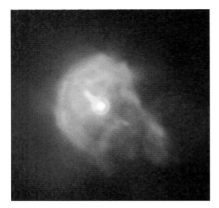

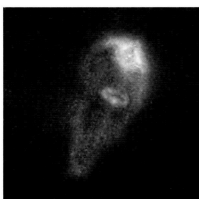

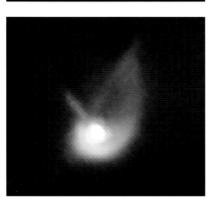

planet Jupiter has only about 1% of the Sun's mass and has not become a star. On the other hand, proto-stars with something like one hundred times the mass of our Sun would be more likely to start runaway nuclear reactions that would blow them apart.

The lifetime and luminosity of a star depends on its mass. Our Sun is burning its fuel at a rate that will give it a lifetime of about 10 billion years – it is currently about five billion years old. However, a star with 10 times the Sun's mass will be about 10 000 times more luminous than the Sun; it therefore has about 10 times more fuel but burns it 10 000 times faster. It will therefore last only about 10 million years. A star with 50 times the Sun's mass would be some 100 000 times brighter than the Sun, but only last for about five million years. Such a star's lifetime would be over in a flash, compared to the constant luminosity of our Sun. The converse of this is also true: a star with only a tenth of the Sun's mass would have less than a thousandth of the Sun's luminosity; it would shine for 1 000 billion years, a period far exceeding the present age of the universe.

Once settled, stars like our Sun maintain uniform luminosity for most of their lives – a necessary condition for the development of life on planets like our Earth. We have evidence on Earth of sedimentary rocks – laid down by liquid water – being formed over three billion years ago, so the energy output of the Sun then must have been similar to its output today.

The demise of stars

The fact that stars run on fuel means that eventually the fuel supply will run out. But rather than die a quiet death, stars end their careers in a blaze of glory. As the hydrogen in the core is depleted, the nuclear reactions shift to a shell surrounding that core. This causes the outer layers of the star to swell enormously and its luminosity to increase. The star becomes a 'red giant', and its diameter may grow hundreds of times larger. Its mass remains, of course, unchanged, so that while it may be very much larger, its outer layers would become extremely tenuous. Our Sun is due to go this way in a few billion years' time. Eventually, the Earth will become too hot to support life. As the Sun progressively swells up (larger and larger), our tiny planet will be incinerated. Our Sun may become so bloated that what would have been the orbit of the Earth might even fit inside it.

In the core of a star close to the end of its lifetime, not only is hydrogen being fused into helium, but helium into carbon, and in time into still heavier elements (but none

Left (top, middle, bottom) Three 'proplyds', believed to be embryonic solar systems

Opposite top The outer layers of a highly evolved star have been ejected to form this 'butterfly' nebula.

Opposite bottom Known as the 'stingray' nebula, this is another example of material ejected from a highly evolved star.

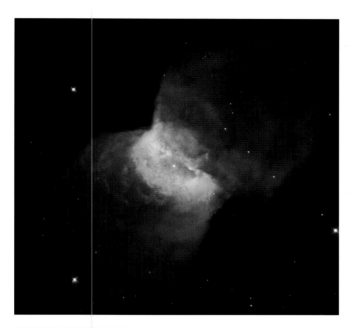

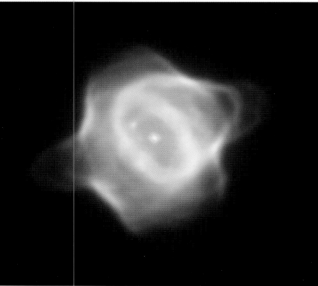

Large and small stars

Stars vary enormously in size and luminosity. The illustration below shows some well-known bright stars in the night sky that are much larger than our Sun. The largest is the red giant star Betelgeuse, so huge that were it put in the centre of our Solar System, the orbit of the Earth would fit inside it. The outer layers of such a star would, however, be extremely tenuous.

Our Sun is shown to be a typical star, even somewhat larger than average. The diagram cannot begin to show the very smallest stars – white dwarf stars that are only about a hundredth of the diameter of our Sun.

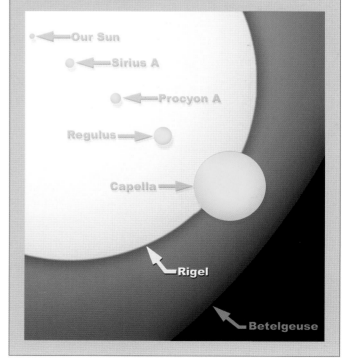

heavier than iron). So much energy is generated from this fusion that the star expands still further, and its outermost layers are pushed away into space. Such stars in the terminal phase of their life are occasionally seen as the objects astronomers call 'planetary nebulae' (see illustrations on page 63), where a shell of gas surrounds the still exceedingly hot core.

In time, all nuclear reactions cease, and the core collapses into a very dense 'white dwarf star'. So much heat is contained within such a body that it would take longer than the present age of the universe to cool below incandescence. White dwarfs are tiny, not much larger than the Earth, yet with densities so high that a teaspoonful would weigh about 500 kilograms.

Meanwhile, what used to be the outer envelope of the star, enriched in the heavier elements that were synthesised inside the star, expands outwards into interstellar space. In time, its motion will be arrested and it will disintegrate and disperse, and intermingle with the gas clouds of the interstellar medium and the debris of other dying stars. In due course, the shock waves – from the spiral compression waves in our galaxy or from 'supernovas' (see below) – will stir the gas, cause condensations to form, and the process of star formation will start over again. Younger stars will be enriched by the elements of older stars, long dead. In this way, most of the material in the galaxy (the normal, known matter, at least) is recycled through generations of stars.

Not all stars end their lives so sedately. Certain particularly massive stars may exhaust all possible nuclear fusion in their cores because they have burnt so fast, leading to a catastrophic collapse of the core, possibly into an incredibly dense 'neutron star' (where one teaspoonful will weigh several million tons). The outer layers of the star would similarly have imploded, only to rebound with increased energy, such that they would subsequently be hurled outwards at thousands of kilometres per second. This is one type of 'supernova' explosion. Another is believed to occur when, in a double star system containing a white dwarf, too much mass is transferred from the other star to the white dwarf, triggering a thermonuclear runaway.

It is just possible that very massive stellar remnants could even collapse to become 'black holes', their gravity so strong that not even light can escape. Certain close double star systems – where one star has already evolved to the end of its lifetime – produce exotic situations. Matter from the more slowly evolving secondary star may be drawn towards, and swirled violently about, the dense companion, producing copious X-ray emissions.

We now understand much about the nature and evolution of stars, but questions remain. Some stars apparently have bi-polar jets that twist and paint remarkable patterns on surrounding interstellar gas. One star – Eta Carina – undergoes massive explosive ejections. We still have a long way to go in understanding such behaviour.

Left *An infrared view reveals a cluster of stars close to the centre of our Galaxy.*

Above A globular cluster may contain hundreds of thousands of stars.

Extrasolar planets

Most of the stars that shine in the night sky ought, like our Sun, to possess planetary systems. Since planets are lit by their parent suns, the light they reflect is so feeble that they would in general appear a billion times fainter than the parent. This makes them impossible to detect telescopically.

Fortunately, there is an alternative way. Consider the case of our Sun and Jupiter, for instance. Although it is commonly said that Jupiter revolves around the Sun, strictly speaking the two bodies revolve (by the laws of physics) around their common centre of mass. That point lies just outside the Sun. Over the period of 12 years that Jupiter takes to complete one revolution of the Sun, the Sun moves around a very much smaller circle, at a speed of only 13 metres a second. By astronomical standards, this is very slow – but nevertheless detectable over a long enough period of time. Extremely accurate and extended measurements of the radial speeds of other stars have, on occasions, revealed periodic oscillations, an indication that the star involved is moving around a centre of mass, and therefore that another body must be present.

In some cases, this other body may be a very low luminosity star (often termed a 'brown dwarf'), but if its mass does not exceed 10 Jupiter masses, it is more likely to be a massive planet. In a few cases, multiple oscillations in speed have suggested the presence of more than a single planet. This technique is biased towards discovering massive planets in orbits close to their parent stars.

CHAPTER 8

Galaxies and large-scale structures

It was once thought to be the entire universe, but the Milky Way – the luminous band of light that stretches across the sky – comes mainly from neighbouring regions in the Galaxy we inhabit. The Galaxy is a massive system of stars, a gigantic disc surrounding a central bulge. Both disc and bulge are packed with stars. Our Sun is an inconspicuous star situated out towards the edge of the disc, as mentioned in the opening chapter and depicted diagrammatically in chapter 3. In the same way that our Earth orbits the Sun, so our Sun and its accompanying Solar System orbits the centre of the Galaxy.

We see the Galaxy from within, its flattened form accounting for the appearance of the Milky Way as an encircling band of luminosity. As in the suburbs of a terrestrial city, neighbouring features dominate or obscure our view. We can see fragments of the neighbouring spiral arms immediately adjacent to our own 'Orion' arm, and very little beyond that. The spiral arms are rich in dust clouds and these clouds are usually opaque. It is a little like not being able to see the wood for the trees. The only exception – as with high skyscrapers in the centre of a city that rise into view – is the central bulge of the Galaxy, which protrudes on either side of the local structure.

In our opening chapter, we showed a diagram suggesting the probable appearance of our Galaxy, and the position of our Solar System (similarly shown in chapter 3). Given the obscuration that mars our view, readers might question the validity of such predictions. The answer is that radio observations – unaffected by dust clouds – have allowed us to map the spiral arms of our Galaxy.

Above *The spiral structure of our Galaxy must be similar to that in this photograph of another spiral galaxy, here seen flat-on. The colour has been adjusted to emphasize the dust lanes in its two major spiral arms, as well as glowing nebulae.*

Our Galaxy is not alone

Our Galaxy is far from unique. There are millions, even billions, of other galaxies.

A galaxy is best described as a city of stars – a city containing about a million million inhabitants. Yet the galaxies of the cosmos are spaced apart from one another like their terrestrial counterparts. Like seeing a city at night from a distance, where one cannot make out individual street lamps, so one cannot normally make out individual stars in a galaxy, save for a few that are exceptionally bright.

Usually the stars in a galaxy's bulge represent an aging population, stars much older than our Sun that were formed long ago. By contrast, the discs of galaxies, especially those with spiral structure, represent a young stellar population, where there is still plenty of interstellar gas and star formation is on-going. The gas provides material for new stars, which are enriched and partly replenished by the shells blown off dying stars, or by the occasional supernova explosion.

Galaxies are probably made up primarily of stars. However, from the manner in which the stars orbit around the centre, it can be deduced that a considerable amount of 'dark matter' must also be present. As the name suggests, this component accounts for a lot of mass, with very little, if any, luminosity. Quite what 'dark matter' is we still do not know. A plausible suggestion is that brown dwarf stars (stars of extremely low luminosity) abound in galaxies, although not all the evidence supports this. Interstellar gas is another major constituent. The gas usually shows a frothy texture, resulting from bubbles blown by hot young stars and supernova explosions. Mixed in with the gas is dust. Many denser clouds appear completely opaque.

The illustrations in this chapter convey something of the diversity of galaxy 'designs'. The most common type is the spiral galaxy. The arms of the spiral are now understood to be regions where interstellar material is compressed, usually leading to star formation. Most of the luminosity in a spiral arm comes from the most massive, but shortest lived, stars. Such stars sometimes ionise surrounding gas, creating a glowing 'nebula' that is mainly red in colour. The central bulges of spiral galaxies see little, if any, star formation. Rather, the general yellow colour of their stellar population indicates that most of the stars are old.

The spiral pattern in a galaxy results from complex wave motions and resonances. Rings and straight bars may sometimes occur, and the pattern is likely to evolve as the galaxy ages. Spiral galaxies are absent from more dense environments, such as clusters of galaxies, which are dominated by elliptical galaxies (as in the illustrations on page 38). Galaxies with discs that lack spiral structure, as though all the interstellar matter had been used up and star formation had ceased, generally occur in dense environments. Elliptical galaxies, which, as their name suggests, simply show an elliptical profile, are populated with older stars.

It is possible that every sizable galaxy (including our own Galaxy) possesses a black hole at its centre – where the mass is so concentrated that not even light can escape. As yet, we do not know which formed first, the galaxy or the black hole. Certain galaxies, however, have 'active nuclei' (see box on page 72).

***Above** A typical spiral galaxy such as this may contain a million million stars. The galaxy is too distant for the stars to be seen individually. Dark dust lanes can be seen interwoven with the star clouds.*

The Milky Way – our Galaxy seen from within – a panorama created from a montage of photographs by Axel Mellinger.

Part of the cosmic sponge

The distribution of galaxies in the cosmos shows a curious labyrinth-like structure, reminiscent of the texture of a bath sponge. The material of the cosmic sponge represents the galaxies, the holes an absence of galaxies. Of course, on this scale, even the galaxies are small entities – and not continuous material – but within the sponge-like, large-scale structures, neighbours are never more than 10 million light years apart. By contrast, there are voids, like the bubbles in the sponge, that are up to 300 million light years across, almost completely devoid of galaxies (see accompanying illustration).

The sponge is not a bad analogy. The voids in a sponge tend to be spherical in shape and interconnected, which is why it is easy to squeeze water in and out. So you could, if you wished, thread your way through the universe by travelling from one void to another. Similarly the 'material' of the sponge is all interconnected (there are no loose bits inside a bath sponge), so you might choose to travel without ever crossing a void.

A sponge is not, however, a perfect analogy. Certain regions of our cosmos seem to be heavier, while the intervening spaces are filled by a lighter frothy texture. These heavier or more densely packed regions are sometimes flattened, and described as 'great walls' or, where appropriate, 'great ribbons'. Complicating the distribution still further is the occasional occurrence of dense clusters of galaxies, like lead shot within the sponge. Usually, such clusters hold a central position within a great wall or great ribbon.

We can model these structures within the cyberspace of a computer, even fly around amongst them. In reality we can no more travel around the large-scale structures than we can travel around our Galaxy. We can only look out from our position. As seen in the accompanying diagram (and in the diagram on page 39), our Galaxy lies towards the fringe of the Local Supercluster or Virgo Supercluster, centred on the Virgo Cluster of galaxies (the name coming from the starry foreground constellation). But even this local large-scale structure is little more than an appendage of a much larger feature I have dubbed the 'Centaurus Wall' (other researchers refer to it as the 'Hypergalaxy'). The Centaurus Wall, as the name implies, is a flattened structure that we see, from the inside, edge-on. It contains the Centaurus Cluster and the very rich Norma Cluster.

Neighbouring features to the Centaurus Wall are the Coma Great Wall that includes the rich Coma Cluster and the Perseus-Pisces Filament (a 'great ribbon') with the dramatic Perseus Cluster.

Below A schematic representation of local large-scale structures; the dots indicate individual galaxies.

Dreaming of still larger structures

As far as we can tell, this sort of structure repeats itself over and over across ever greater distances. It is still a matter of debate whether even larger structures exist. Also much debated is whether large-scale structures form before galaxies take shape, or whether the galaxies form first and afterwards gather into large-scale structures. Dubbed 'top-down' and 'bottom-up', these two competing scenarios may both be partly valid. When gravity alone is at work, it tends to form the smaller structures first, and so work from the bottom up. Conversely, if enough 'hot dark matter' were present in the universe, it would wipe out the smaller structures. A pure top-down scenario would suggest that the galaxies formed only recently, whereas there is evidence (presented in chapter 9) that suggests that there were galaxies in existence throughout most of the history of the universe.

There is still much to be understood about the formation of galaxies and the texture of the cosmic tapestry.

Above *Galaxies can occasionally collide or graze one another as this example shows.*

Right *An unusual polar ring galaxy*

Active galaxies

Of the galaxies we see about us, about one or two percent can be said to be 'active'. (Our Galaxy, the Milky Way, is not active at the moment.) This means that they emit a considerable amount of light or radio radiation over and above the normal contribution from stars and interstellar gas. The energy that drives such activity originates in the very heart or nucleus of active galaxies. In spite of the enormous energies involved, such 'active galactic nuclei' are physically very small. The only possible explanation known to science is that they are massive black holes – each millions of times heavier than our Sun. By definition, light cannot escape from a black hole itself, but its extreme gravity pulls in surrounding material, which is violently accelerated. An active nucleus occurs when matter swirls in towards a black hole, in the process creating highly energetic radiation or extreme electrical voltages.

Active galactic nuclei often manifest themselves as having extreme luminosity, in which case they are termed quasars. Quasars are the brightest sustained objects in the universe and may be bright enough to mask their host galaxies. This allows us to see them at great distances, and at times when the universe was much younger. Nearer galaxies, which are seen closer to us in time, show fewer incidences of active nuclei. From this we have deduced that such quasar activity was more common in the past, leading us to suspect very strongly that every major galaxy has a black hole at its centre – including our own.

Some active nuclei have less luminosity, but emit two powerful jets (possibly accelerated by high voltages) in opposite directions. The jets are more usually visible to radio, rather than optical telescopes, and normally carry well clear of the galaxy, before breaking up and dispersing their energy into 'radio lobes' on either side of the host galaxy.

Right and below Examples where quasar nuclei outshine their host galaxies

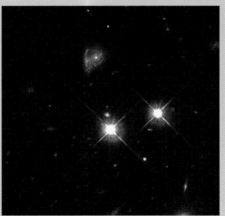

Falling for the Great Attractor

Large-scale structures give rise to large-scale movement. A large concentration of galaxies formed in a 'great wall' or 'supercluster' has the gravitational power of attraction to draw in surrounding galaxies. By contrast, voids, because they lack the mass needed to provide such gravity, effectively repel galaxies. Gravity, or lack of it, sets galaxies in motion.

Our entire Galaxy is moving at 600 kilometres per second, relative to our local 'frame of rest'. Part of that motion is caused by the gravitational attraction of the nearby Virgo Cluster of galaxies. There is, however, no danger of our ever falling into the Virgo Cluster, since it is moving away from us at 1 000 kilometres per second as the universe expands (see chapter 9). Our Galaxy seems to be moving more in the direction of the Centaurus constellation, towards a region dubbed the 'Great Attractor' – which may simply be the Centaurus Wall. This is somewhat baffling, since we cannot see sufficient galaxies to account for the gravitational pull. It is also not understood why the equally massive Perseus-Pisces Ribbon – in the opposite direction – does not have a stronger effect.

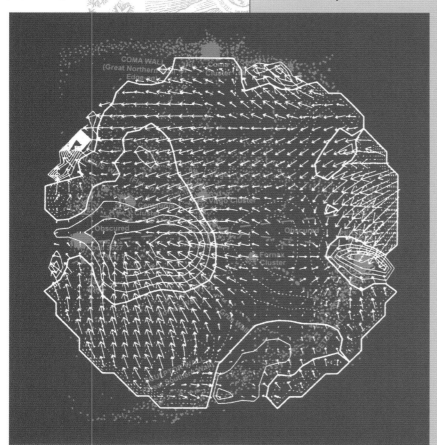

Arrows superimposed on the earlier map of nearby large-scale structures indicate the streaming of galaxies. The convergence towards the Great Attractor region (left of centre) is apparent; similarly, there are flows towards Perseus-Pisces (right) and the Coma Wall (top). (Adapted from a map by LN da Costa and collaborators.)

CHAPTER 9

The cosmos

We know that the universe, in its present form, has not always existed; nor can it exist forever. Stars need fuel to keep shining – as do lamps to keep burning – and there is only so much fuel in the universe. We know already that stars are not forming at as fast a rate as they did several billion years back. In terms of star formation and abundance of starlight, the universe is somewhat 'over the hill' – and the situation is unlikely to improve in the future. The decline will continue until all star formation ceases. Eventually, even the longest-lasting low-mass stars will burn out, and the universe will become a dark, dark place, quite unfit for human habitation.

Early in the 20th century, astronomer Vesto Slipher discovered that almost all the surrounding galaxies were receding from us, at many hundreds, or even thousands, of kilometres a second. The famous astronomer Edwin Hubble, who calibrated distances to galaxies, was able to show that the velocity of recession of a galaxy is directly proportional to its distance from us – the more distant a galaxy is from Earth, the faster it appears to be moving away.

At first sight, it might appear as if our Galaxy were particularly unpopular, with every galaxy in flight away from it. But the relationship discovered by Hubble does not mean that our Galaxy is the point away from which all other galaxies are moving. Rather all galaxies, ours included, are spacing themselves further apart from each other. An appetising analogy is that of a fruit cake being baked. Let the currants represent the galaxies. Then, as the cake grows larger and larger, so the currants are spaced further and further apart from one another.

But here is the difficult part. Even Hubble supposed that, like gymnasts securing adequate space for themselves in a hall, the galaxies were moving outwards to occupy previously empty space. However, that was not the case. Albert Einstein had already brought a new understanding as to how space itself behaves: he found it could expand like the *dough* of the analogous fruit cake! The galaxies are not in themselves moving in space, rather the space in which they are situated, like the dough of the cake, is expanding.

If the expansion of the universe could be reversed and run backwards in time, the galaxies would start getting closer to one another. Run back far enough, the whole of the universe would come together. In other words, the expansion of the universe is an indication that the universe started in a compact, very dense state (according to the laws of physics, it was also very hot) and has been expanding ever since. This is known as the 'big-bang' hypothesis, the widely accepted paradigm of modern cosmology.

There are a number of ways in which we can tell the age of the universe or, at least, the age of the universe in its current form. One is that suggested above: reversing the universal trend of expansion to run backwards, contracting at the same rate as the current rate of expansion. Another is to determine the ages of the oldest stars, which obviously must be somewhat younger than the universe itself. Yet another is to measure nuclear isotope ratios. All three methods show reasonable agreement – that the universe is somewhere in the range of 12 to 17 billion years old. Fifteen billion is a good, round, convenient figure to use.

Will the universe ever re-collapse? It now seems highly unlikely. Measurements in the past decade show that the universe has too little mass in it to exert enough gravitational braking. Moreover, recent measurements involving 'supernova'

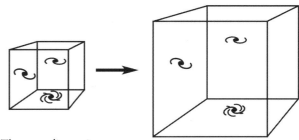

The expanding universe

explosions in distant galaxies indicate that, far from slowing down, the rate of expansion is still accelerating. Some as yet mysterious force is apparently still driving it.

One of the reasons why we have a fairly good understanding of how the universe has evolved is because we can map its history. We can see the universe not only as it is now, but as it was in the past. This overview is made possible by the fact that light travels at a finite speed of 300 000 kilometres per second – very fast by terrestrial standards, but fairly sedate by astronomical standards. As pointed out earlier (in chapter 3), many of the stars in the night sky appear not as they are at this moment, but as they were years ago, because of the time that it has taken light to travel from those stars to the Earth. Similarly, we see the centre of our Galaxy as it was 30 000 years ago.

When it comes to other galaxies, we look millions of light years out in distance, and correspondingly millions of years back in time. For example, the Virgo Cluster of galaxies is seen as it was 50 million years ago, and the Coma Cluster as it was 350 million years ago. Peering ever deeper into the cosmos, we penetrate billions of light years out, and billions of years back into time. The deepest we have ever seen is with help from the Hubble Space Telescope that has looked out into the cosmos in opposite directions, and captured the view photographically, with 'exposure times' of over ten days. Those two photographs (reproduced here) reveal galaxies that are, on average, several billion light years out, at a time when the universe was only half its present age. At first, the galaxies revealed in these images look similar to galaxies of today, but more detailed analysis has revealed significant differences. So we are able to see how galaxies have evolved.

The most distant objects in the Hubble Deep Field are probably seen as they were about 12 billion years back, only a couple of billion years or so after the 'big bang' itself. Bigger telescopes may let us look deeper, but we do not expect to see much in the way of galaxies because we will be looking back to an era when galaxies were only beginning to form.

Remarkably, we have already been able to see further back – to see a distorted, but nevertheless accurate, portrait of the universe only 300 000 years after the 'big bang' itself, and long

These two Hubble Deep Field photographs, looking in opposite directions in the sky (left north, right south), show the universe in the past.

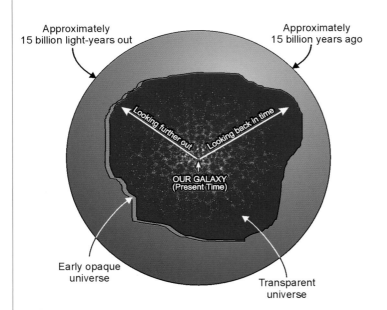

Approximately 15 billion light-years out

Approximately 15 billion years ago

Looking further out

Looking back in time

OUR GALAXY
(Present Time)

Early opaque universe

Transparent universe

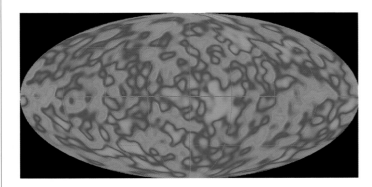

Top The 'Cosmic Egg'

Above The picture on the inside of the 'Cosmic Egg'. Very slight fluctuations, recorded by the COBE satellite, are greatly exaggerated.

before galaxies started to form. This comes about because, following the 'big bang', the material content of the universe (now known to be almost entirely hydrogen and helium gas) was hot and dense. Conditions then, throughout the entire universe, were not unlike present-day conditions inside our Sun. Clearly we could not have existed in such conditions.

The key aspect is that the gas would have been opaque – one would only have been able to see a limited distance through it. In the same way, one cannot today look into the centre of the Sun, even though it is made of gas. But as the universe expanded, so it became less dense, and cooled – and cleared. There would come a point, about 300 000 years after the 'big bang', when the gas filling the universe changed from being opaque to transparent. The universe has remained transparent ever since.

So we can look deeper and deeper into space, until we reach a point where and when the universe becomes opaque – forming a wall through which we cannot see. In fact, rather than a wall, it will appear to us as a spherical shell, centred on the Earth and with a radius of some 15 billion light years. It encloses us as would the shell of an egg. (Such an image forms the basis for this author's book entitled *Cosmology Revealed: Living inside the Cosmic Egg.*)

The inside 'surface' of the shell carries a picture of the early universe, recorded at a time when the universe changed from opaque to transparent. It is somewhat like having a single picture of a child, without seeing what the child was like as a baby, or what sort of adult it later grew up to be. The picture ought to be blazing light, since the universe then was nearly as hot as the surface of our Sun now is. But the expansion of the universe has shifted the radiation from visible light to microwaves, known as 'Cosmic Background Radiation'. Were our eyes sensitive to microwaves, then the sky would be seen to be bright all over. Though distorted by stretching, the picture in the inside of the 'Cosmic Egg' is almost completely uniform. Only very close scrutiny has revealed the smallest of fluctuations. Some of those fluctuations must have seeded the great superclusters of today.

What lies beyond the shell of the Cosmic Egg we cannot see and will not know.

Why is the sky so dark?

It is a reasonable question to an obvious observation: why is the sky so dark? The answer tells us much about the universe we inhabit.

It used to be thought that the universe was full of stars. We now know it is full of galaxies, which are full of stars. Suppose we choose a line of view out into space. That line might pass outwards between stars, and between stars in other galaxies. But, providing the universe is large enough, it would eventually collide with a star. The surface brightness of a star's disc does not diminish with distance, so the sky in the direction we have chosen would be as bright as that star's disc – and roughly as bright as the Sun's disc. Since the same would be true for any lines of sight that we might choose, directed in whichever direction in the sky, then the entire sky should be as bright as the disc of our Sun. And we would be fried alive!

Happily that is not the case. But what shields us? Thick dust clouds might do so, but they would soon be heated to the same temperature as the stars. Rather, as we now understand it, the expansion of the universe robs the light of energy – not only the light from stars, but the light from the early, dense, incandescent universe. Thanks to the expansion of the universe, we are able to exist in comfort. Furthermore, so dramatic is the effect, that the night sky – between the visible stars – appears to be quite black.

Gravity and antigravity

Everybody is familiar with the attractive force of gravity. Since the time of Isaac Newton, we have known that gravity works on ever larger scales. It not only keeps us firmly on the ground but also controls the way the planets move round the Sun, and the way that the Solar System moves around the Galaxy. It even causes the large-scale streaming of galaxies (see Falling for the Great Attractor on page 73).

On the other hand, antigravity (repulsion instead of attraction) had seemed to exist only in the realm of science fiction – but not any longer. In the early 20th century, when it was generally believed that the universe was static, Einstein introduced the notion of antigravity to balance and counteract exactly the gravitational forces between galaxies. However, soon after that, the fact that the universe is expanding was discovered, and the concept of antigravity was no longer needed – at least not until the late 1990s, when observations of distant supernova explosions suggested it might exist.

These distant supernovas appear systematically fainter than they ought to be. The most likely explanation is that the expansion of the universe has speeded up, instead of slowing down as previously expected. In other words, some form of antigravity is working on the universe as a whole, accelerating the expansion. Unfortunately, we have as yet no idea what exactly antigravity is and quite how it operates, although speculations tend to treat it as 'dark energy'. If antigravity were to follow Einstein's original premise, then its effect should get even stronger as the universe expands further. More detailed measurements of supernovas, in the years ahead, should help trace the manner in which the universe has expanded, and throw some light on this mysterious force.

CHAPTER 10

Telescopes and observatories

Most people think of a telescope as something that magnifies distant objects. Magnification is indeed useful for seeing the Moon and planets, or even 'double stars', but is of no use whatsoever when it comes to individual stars. The truth is that individual stars are so very distant that, when viewed with the naked eye or through a telescope, they still look like pinpoints of light.

In fact, with higher magnification, stars appear not quite as pinpoints but rather as somewhat fuzzy blobs, due to the blurring caused by the Earth's atmosphere. Because we are obliged to peer through a layer of atmosphere, multimillion Rand telescopes can magnify no more than the telescopes sold by the local pharmacy. It was the desire to view outer space from beyond our atmosphere that prompted the expenditure of so much money in sending up the Hubble Space telescope.

Why then, one might ask, spend money on bigger telescopes? The reason is to collect more light. The size of a telescope is assessed not by its magnification, but by how much light it can collect. The bigger the aperture of a telescope, the fainter the object it can see, and the further into space it can penetrate. In a way, the human eye is like a telescope; it has a maximum aperture of about 6 millimetres. Most amateur astronomers use instruments with apertures from 60–300 millimetres, and professional astronomers use ones with apertures from 0,5–10 metres. That means that the largest telescopes can gather some three million times more light than the human eye – no wonder they see so far into space.

The aperture of a telescope relates to the diameter of its primary lens or mirror, which determines the amount of light (radiation) that enters it. The optical design can take a variety of forms according to considerations such as field of view and cost. The traditional refractor – the sort of instrument Nelson would have raised to his eye – uses a large (and relatively expensive) lens to collect light. Late in the 17th century, Newton invented the reflecting telescope, which uses concave mirrors. The reflecting telescope is cheaper to manufacture, and has replaced the earlier refracting instrument in a professional capacity since the early 20th century. Reflecting telescopes have a large primary concave mirror, very accurately figured. Able to be mechanically supported from underneath, mirrors can be made larger than the largest lens possible.

Given the expense of large professional telescopes, they are located in climates that are largely cloud-free and at considerable altitude (for optimum performance with minimal interference from the Earth's atmosphere). Because of such site selection criteria, most of the world's major telescopes are located around latitudes 30° north and south of the Equator, while the volcanic islands of Hawaii and the Canaries are also favoured sites. In southern Africa, the higher plateaux of the Karoo are prime sites (see box on page 80).

While most amateur astronomers still look through the eyepiece of a telescope, such a practice has long ceased in the professional world. Late in the 19th century, photographic emulsion was found to be a far superior means of recording images. Moreover, by increasing the exposure time, faint light could be accumulated so that far more was revealed than ever the eye could see. Gone were the canals on Mars and other figments of the imagination that coloured visual observations. Instead, interstellar nebulae and the spiral structure of other galaxies were revealed. Late in the 20th century, the 'charge-coupled detector' (CCD) largely replaced photographic emulsion; today, almost all data is digital and processed by computers.

In terms of light-gathering power, the advent of CCD devices (and the electronic image detectors that preceded them) has been a great breakthrough. Photographic emulsion was at best only capable of registering a few percent of the photons of light that struck it. By contrast CCDs are typically 80% or better in efficiency. As a result, even the largest telescopes of the 1950s would be completely outclassed by modest telescopes of today.

The telescope is an essential component in the bid to photograph our skies. While the entire sky has been photographed at modest resolution by wide-angle telescopes (still using photographic plates, because they are so much larger than CCDs), there is a need to see much more detail in individual objects. Further CCD images allow precise measurements of brightness and colour – considered essential by astronomers. Variations in a star's brightness, both large and very small, also reveal a wealth of information on the behaviour of stars as they evolve.

Another useful type of technology is spectroscopy, whereby the light of a star or galaxy is dispersed into a spectrum. It gives us insight into the physical conditions within the object, as well as providing a means for measuring its speed either towards or away from us. For instance the 'redshifting' of spectral features in galaxies tells us about the expansion of the universe (see chapter 9).

Nevertheless, visible light, as physicists know, is only a small part of the electromagnetic spectrum, albeit the most abundant radiation emitted by stars such as our Sun. Specialized telescopes have been designed to operate outside visible light, registering, for example, infrared, and still longer-wavelength radiation such as micro- and radio waves. Shorter wavelengths can also be detected, such as ultra-violet, X-rays or even gamma rays. There is much to be gained from operating in these other regions of the spectrum, as they are complementary to optical investigations. For instance, radio waves let us see cold interstellar gas, rather than stars; infrared lets us see dust; X-rays show us extremely hot gas, as in the corona that surrounds our Sun; while X-rays and gamma rays reveal exotic high-energy happenings. Curiously, the most abundant radiation in the universe is not light, but microwaves, a remnant from the hot early universe.

Unfortunately, the Earth's atmosphere is not necessarily transparent to all these different sorts of radiation – some have to be studied from spacecraft. However, radio astronomy, like optical astronomy, can be pursued from the surface of the Earth, and many radio telescopes have consequently been built. In principle, they follow the same design as optical telescopes, generally using concave mirrors. But because radio waves are so much longer than optical waves, the required accuracy is not nearly as exacting, and mirrors can be made of metal sheeting, even mesh. The mirrors can also be much bigger, 100 metres in diameter or more. If the mirror is held stationary, as in the Arecibo Telescope in Puerto Rico, an aperture of 300 metres is possible. With such large apertures, radio telescopes generally exceed the sensitivity of optical telescopes.

A drawback of radio telescopes is that a single such telescope produces a very blurred (low resolution) image, considerably less clear than that produced by the human eye. However, signals from several radio telescopes can be merged to overcome this problem; the further apart the telescopes, the better the picture. Radio telescopes on different continents, all aimed at the same target, can produce exceptionally detailed pictures when their signals are merged.

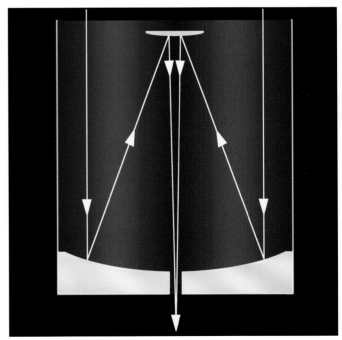

Most large professional telescopes employ this 'Cassegrain' design. Light, captured by the concave primary mirror, travels back up the telescope to a convex secondary mirror, then down the telescope and through a central hole in the primary mirror, where it is brought to a focus.

The South African Astronomical Observatory

Southern Africa is a particularly good place to carry out astronomical observations. The climate is relatively dry, the night sky generally unpolluted by artificial light, and the air usually very clear. The Karoo is particularly good, especially its higher elevations, where horizontal visibility can often exceed 150 kilometres. Furthermore, southern Africa is strategically placed – together with South America and Australia – as one of three continents with access to the southern skies. However, because of the separation in longitude, southern Africa may provide sole access to a particular area of the southern sky at a given time.

Consequently, in years gone by, a number of observatories were established, chiefly as southern stations for northern institutions and universities. These included the Royal Observatory in Cape Town (run by the British Admiralty); the Radcliffe Observatory in Pretoria (Oxford University); the Boyden (Harvard) and Lamont-Hussey (Michigan) Observatories, both near Bloemfontein; the Leiden Southern Station near Johannesburg (Holland); and the Yale Station in Johannesburg. In addition, South Africa's own national observatory (the Union Observatory, later renamed the Republic Observatory) was situated in urban Johannesburg. Hence almost all of these were located in or close to cities, and their operations were affected and jeopardized by the great increase in city lighting in the 1960s.

In 1972, the South African Astronomical Observatory was founded by the merger of the Royal Observatory and the Republic Observatory, with the addition of the Radcliffe Observatory soon after. The Royal Observatory survived as the headquarters of the new institution but all viable telescopes were relocated to a site just outside the small Karoo town of Sutherland. There on a flat hilltop plateau are 1,9, 1,0, 0,6 and 0,5 metre telescopes, constantly manned by four or more astronomers. In more recent years, two small robotic telescopes have been added, one to monitor the Sun (University of Birmingham) and one to carry out photometric observations. In 2000, the Japanese added a 1,4 metre infrared telescope. That same year saw the start of construction of the giant Southern African Large Telescope (see box opposite).

The astronomers normally work a week at a time, observing all night and sleeping in the daytime in specially darkened rooms of the hostel. The observatory, however, has to have substantial technical support, involving numerous electronic and mechanical engineering specialists who work mainly by day.

Aerial views of the 'constellation' of telescopes and related buildings at Sutherland. The high altitude and clear skies make this an ideal site for starwatching.

The Southern African Large Telescope

Due for completion at the end of 2004, the Southern African Large Telescope (SALT), with an aperture just exceeding 10 metres, will be on a par with the largest telescopes in the world. It is based on the Hobby-Eberly telescope in Texas, which uses a revolutionary cost-saving design. Its primary mirror is spherical and is composed of 91 identical hexagonal segments. The segments are positioned under active computer control. The telescope is held within a light metal frame requiring no heavy engineering since, when in use, it does not move – unlike all conventional telescopes that are aimed at targets and then track as the Earth rotates. Instead of the telescope's moving, a light mobile tracker at the top end of the telescope follows objects in the focal plane. The tracker incorporates an optical system to correct for the aberration caused by a spherical mirror, and carries two of the instruments – a spectrograph and a camera.

The design is based on the Arecibo Radio Telescope in Puerto Rico, which has a fixed reflector mirror, constructed in a natural hollow, and aimed directly upward. SALT does not aim directly upward, but is slanted over by 37° from the vertical. This is because the telescope can be lifted by airbags off its four legs, spun around and set looking in a different position. Thus the telescope can observe anywhere in a ring, centred overhead, with a radius of 37°, and a width of about 12°. The tracker can follow objects for an hour or longer, depending on their position in the sky.

Alongside the telescope stands a 'collimation' tower. The telescope can be aimed at the top of the tower and effectively observes an artificial star while its mirrors are aligned.

The telescope is being sited at the South African Astronomical Observatory. It represents an international collaboration between South Africa and universities and institutions in the United States, Poland, Germany, New Zealand and the United Kingdom. The public will be welcome to visit the facility during the daytime, and will be able to see the telescope from a special viewing gallery.

Construction is nearing completion on the largest single telescope in the southern hemisphere, with a hexagonal mirror array 11 metres across. It will be able to record distant stars, galaxies and quasars a billion times too faint to be seen with the unaided eye – as faint as a candle flame at the distance of the moon.

Top left SALT under construction, June 2002
Bottom left This cutaway view shows the telescope inside its housing

Star maps

This section contains 12 star maps, appropriate for all 12 months and any time of the night. To decide which map to use, consult the table below, or see notes accompanying the individual maps. The maps can be used anywhere in the southern hemisphere; strictly speaking, they are set for latitude 30° south.

The centre of each map is the point in the sky overhead, the circular edge of the map is the horizon. Ideally, you should hold the map (facing downwards) above your head, and rotate it so that north on the map matches the direction north, east on the map matches east, etc. You will only get this to happen holding the map above you, not if you lay it on a table (because the cardinal points of the compass are reversed compared to a geographical map). However, reading a map above your head is not exactly comfortable, and there is an easier way. Look at the printed labels on the map and you will see that they follow around with the circular horizon. Simply hold the map in front of you and if, for instance, you are facing west, rotate the map until you can read 'LOOKING WEST' the right way up. You can then easily read the names of constellations above the western horizon. If, on the other hand, you are looking south, then rotate the map until the book is upside down, but the 'LOOKING SOUTH' label, and the names of constellations above the southern horizon, are upright.

Your time of observation may not exactly match the time at which the map is set, so objects may be slightly higher or lower above the eastern or western horizons. Similarly, if your latitude is slightly different from 30° south, objects may be slightly higher or lower above the northern and southern horizons.

Ideally, these maps should be printed inside a hollow hemisphere resembling the dome of a planetarium. Flattening the maps onto a sheet has resulted in slight distortion of the shapes of the constellations.

The maps do not show the position of the Moon and visible planets (which resemble bright stars), as these change from month to month, and their configurations do not repeat each year. For this reason, the planetarium in Cape Town issues a version of these maps each month that also shows the Moon and planets.

Which map number to use at different times of the night

	19h	21h	23h	01h	03h	05h
Jan		1	2	3	4	5
Feb	1	2	3	4	5	6
Mar	2	3	4	5	6	7
Apr	3	4	5	6	7	8
May	4	5	6	7	8	9
Jun	5	6	7	8	9	10
Jul	6	7	8	9	10	11
Aug	7	8	9	10	11	12
Sep	8	9	10	11	12	1
Oct	9	10	11	12	1	2
Nov	10	11	12	1	2	3
Dec		12	1	2	3	4

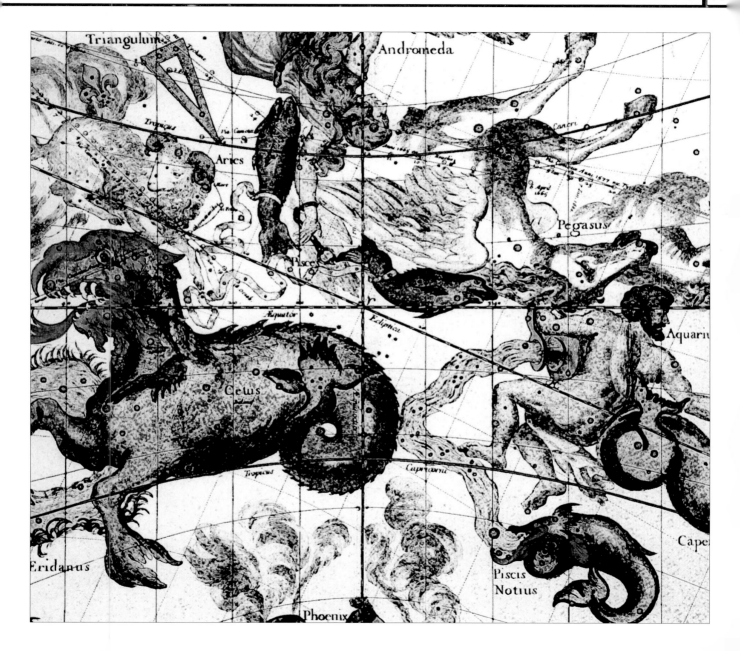

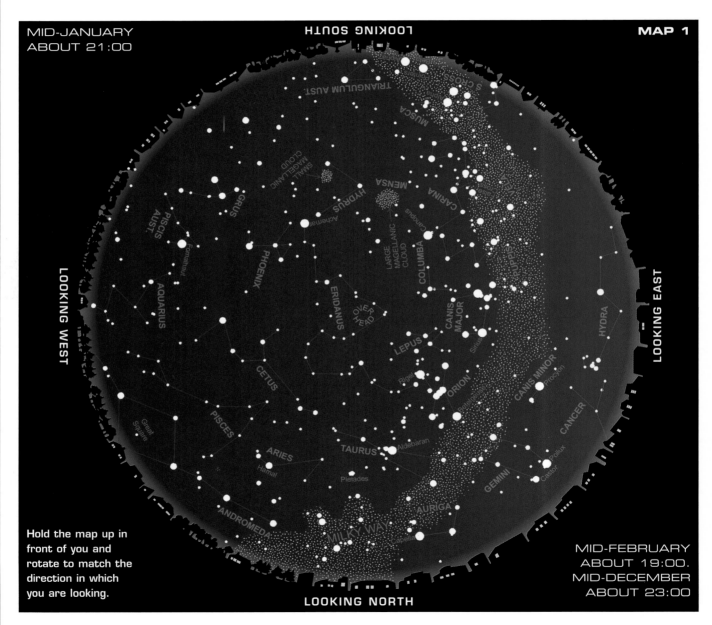

MID-JANUARY
ABOUT 21:00

LOOKING SOUTH

MAP 1

TRIANGULUM AUST.

S CROSS

MUSCA

SMALL MAGELLANIC CLOUD

MENSA

HYDRUS

Achernar

GRUS

CARINA

VELA

PISCIS AUST.

Fomalhaut

PHOENIX

LARGE MAGELLANIC CLOUD

Canopus

PUPPIS

AQUARIUS

ERIDANUS

OVER HEAD

COLUMBA

CANIS MAJOR

LOOKING WEST

CETUS

LEPUS

Sirius

HYDRA

Rigel

ORION

CANIS MINOR

Procyon

LOOKING EAST

PISCES

Betelgeuse

CANCER

Great Square

ARIES

Hamal

TAURUS

Aldebaran

GEMINI

Castor

Pollux

ANDROMEDA

Pleiades

AURIGA

Capella

MILKY WAY

Hold the map up in
front of you and
rotate to match the
direction in which
you are looking.

MID-FEBRUARY
ABOUT 19:00.
MID-DECEMBER
ABOUT 23:00

LOOKING NORTH

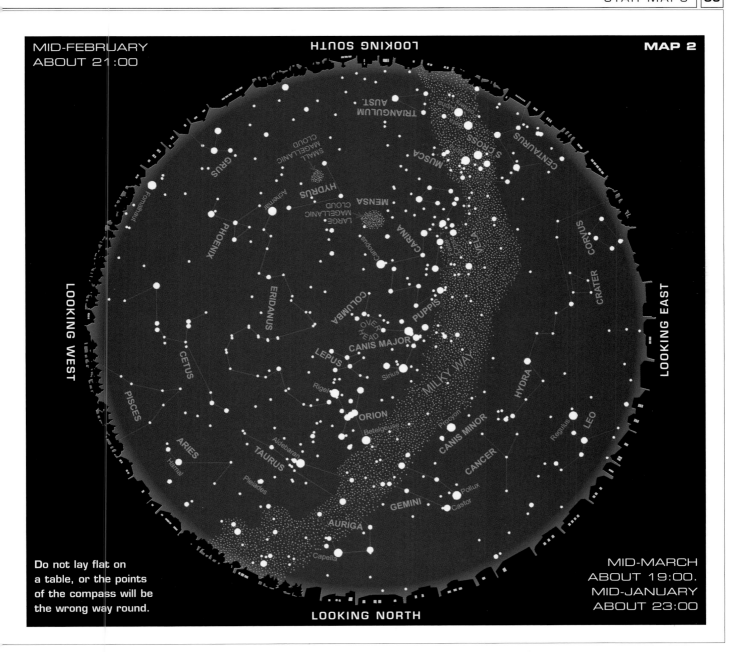

MID-FEBRUARY
ABOUT 21:00

LOOKING SOUTH

MAP 2

LOOKING WEST

LOOKING EAST

Do not lay flat on
a table, or the points
of the compass will be
the wrong way round.

MID-MARCH
ABOUT 19:00.
MID-JANUARY
ABOUT 23:00

LOOKING NORTH

TRIANGULUM AUST.

SMALL MAGELLANIC CLOUD

MUSCA

S CROSS

CENTAURUS

GRUS

HYDRUS

MENSA

LARGE MAGELLANIC CLOUD

CARINA

VELA

CORVUS

PHOENIX

Fomalhaut

Achernar

Canopus

CRATER

ERIDANUS

COLUMBA

PUPPIS

HYDRA

CETUS

OVER HEAD

CANIS MAJOR

MILKY WAY

LEO

LEPUS

Rigel

Sirius

Procyon

Regulus

PISCES

ORION

Betelgeuse

CANIS MINOR

ARIES

Aldebaran

TAURUS

CANCER

Hamal

Pollux

Pleiades

GEMINI

Castor

AURIGA

Capella

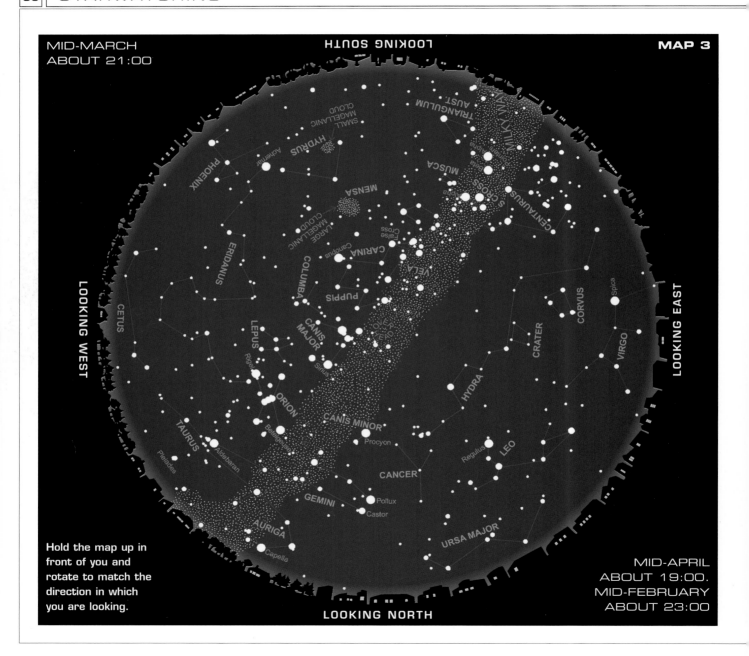

MID-MARCH
ABOUT 21:00

LOOKING SOUTH

MAP 3

LOOKING WEST

LOOKING EAST

LOOKING NORTH

Hold the map up in front of you and rotate to match the direction in which you are looking.

MID-APRIL
ABOUT 19:00.
MID-FEBRUARY
ABOUT 23:00

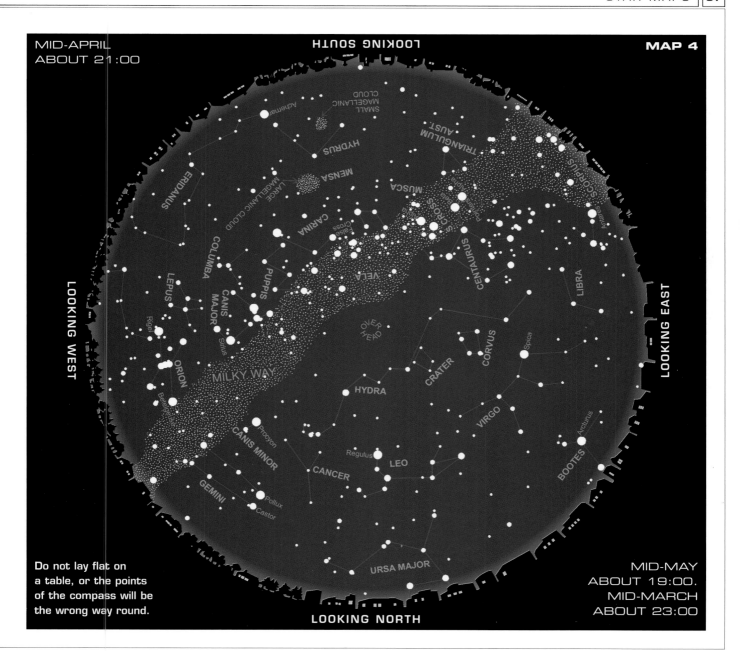

MID-APRIL
ABOUT 21:00

LOOKING SOUTH

MAP 4

LOOKING WEST

LOOKING EAST

LOOKING NORTH

Do not lay flat on
a table, or the points
of the compass will be
the wrong way round.

MID-MAY
ABOUT 19:00.
MID-MARCH
ABOUT 23:00

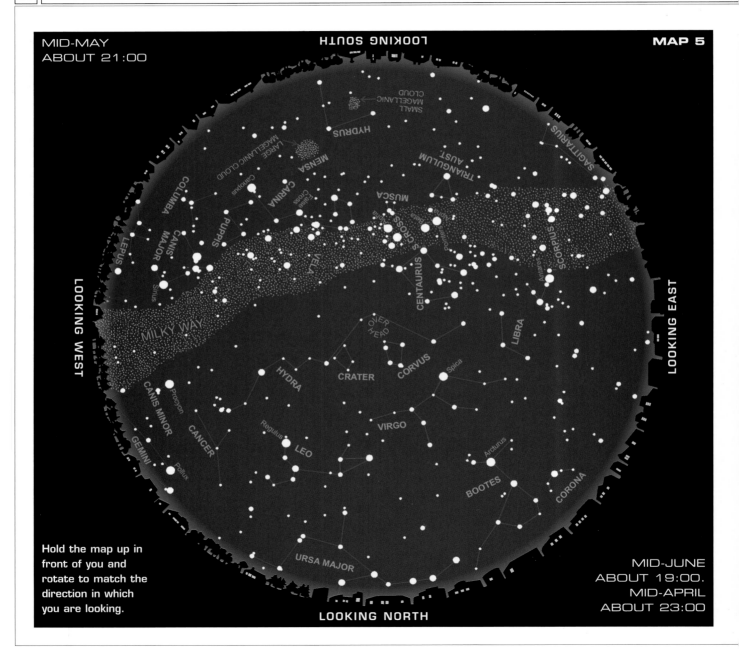

MID-MAY
ABOUT 21:00

LOOKING SOUTH

MAP 5

LOOKING WEST

LOOKING EAST

MILKY WAY

SMALL MAGELLANIC CLOUD

HYDRUS

MENSA

LARGE MAGELLANIC CLOUD

CARINA

COLUMBA

LEPUS

CANIS MAJOR

Sirius

PUPPIS

Canopus

False Cross

VELA

CRUX S. CROSS

CENTAURUS

MUSCA

TRIANGULUM AUST.

SAGITTARIUS

SCORPIUS

Antares

LIBRA

OVER HEAD

CRATER

CORVUS

Spica

HYDRA

CANIS MINOR

Procyon

CANCER

Regulus

LEO

VIRGO

Arcturus

GEMINI

Pollux

BOOTES

CORONA

URSA MAJOR

Hold the map up in
front of you and
rotate to match the
direction in which
you are looking.

LOOKING NORTH

MID-JUNE
ABOUT 19:00.
MID-APRIL
ABOUT 23:00

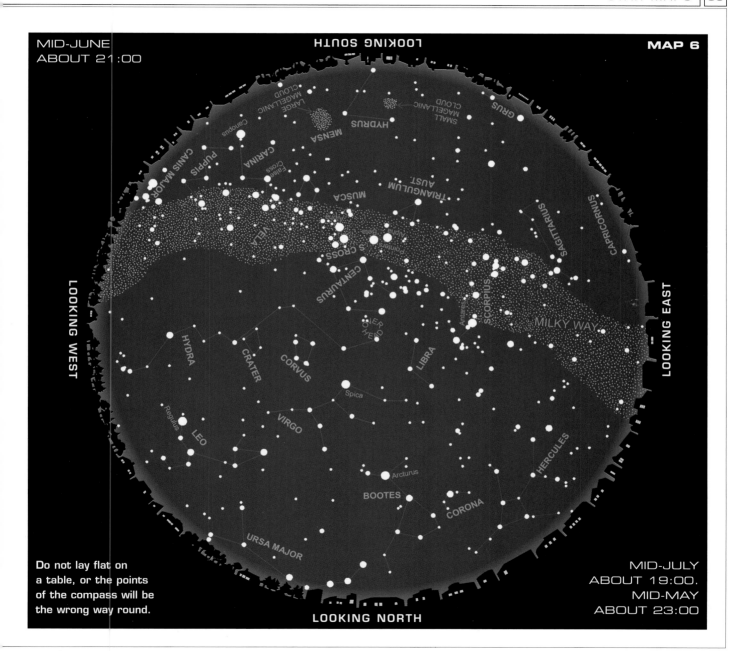

MID-JUNE
ABOUT 21:00

LOOKING SOUTH

MAP 6

LOOKING WEST

LOOKING EAST

Do not lay flat on
a table, or the points
of the compass will be
the wrong way round.

MID-JULY
ABOUT 19:00.
MID-MAY
ABOUT 23:00

LOOKING NORTH

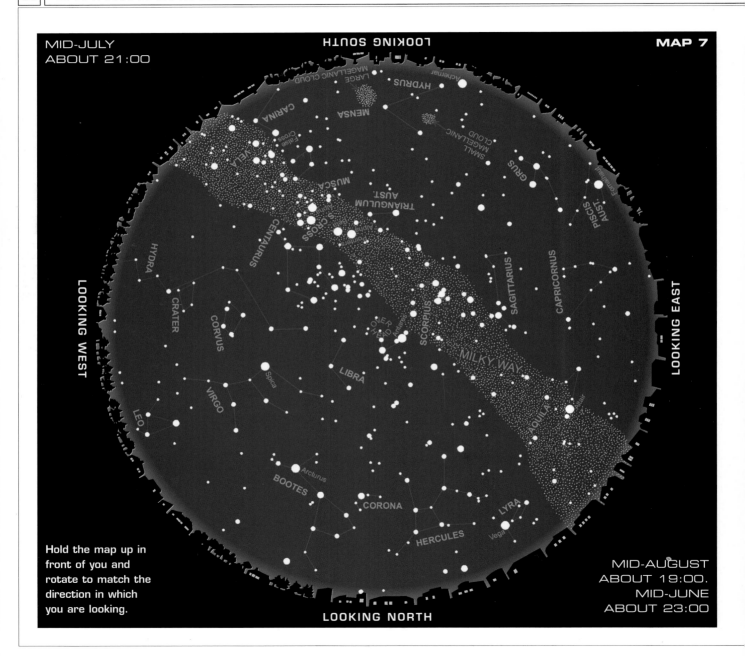

MID-JULY
ABOUT 21:00

LOOKING SOUTH

MAP 7

LOOKING WEST

LOOKING EAST

LOOKING NORTH

Hold the map up in front of you and rotate to match the direction in which you are looking.

MID-AUGUST
ABOUT 19:00.
MID-JUNE
ABOUT 23:00

CARINA
VELA
FALSE CROSS
MENSA
HYDRUS
LARGE MAGELLANIC CLOUD
Achernar
SMALL MAGELLANIC CLOUD
GRUS
MUSCA
CRUX (S. CROSS)
TRIANGULUM AUST.
Gacrux
CENTAURUS
Alpha & Beta Centauri
PISCIS AUST.
Fomalhaut
HYDRA
CAPRICORNUS
SAGITTARIUS
CRATER
CORVUS
OPHIUCHUS
Antares
SCORPIUS
MILKY WAY
VIRGO
LIBRA
AQUILA
Altair
LEO
Spica
Arcturus
BOOTES
CORONA
HERCULES
LYRA
Vega

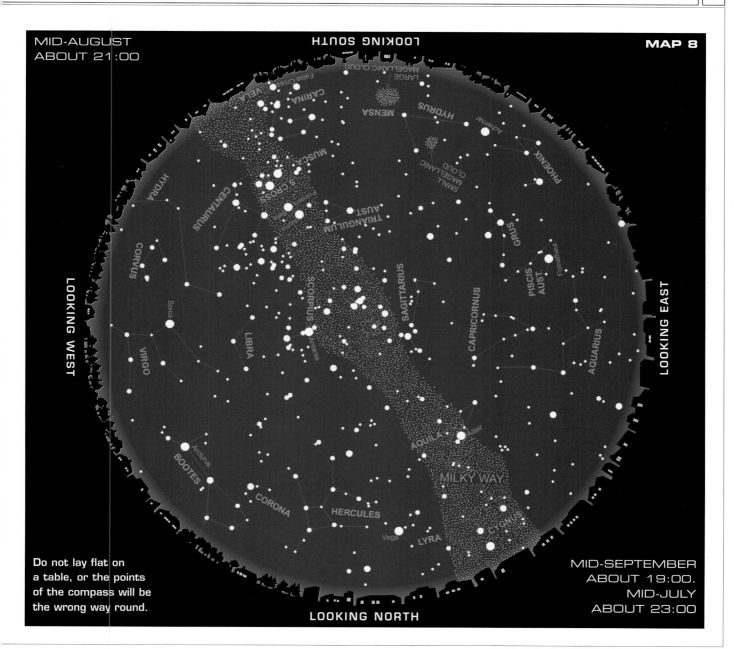

MID-AUGUST
ABOUT 21:00

LOOKING SOUTH

MAP 8

LOOKING WEST

LOOKING EAST

Do not lay flat on
a table, or the points
of the compass will be
the wrong way round.

MID-SEPTEMBER
ABOUT 19:00.
MID-JULY
ABOUT 23:00

LOOKING NORTH

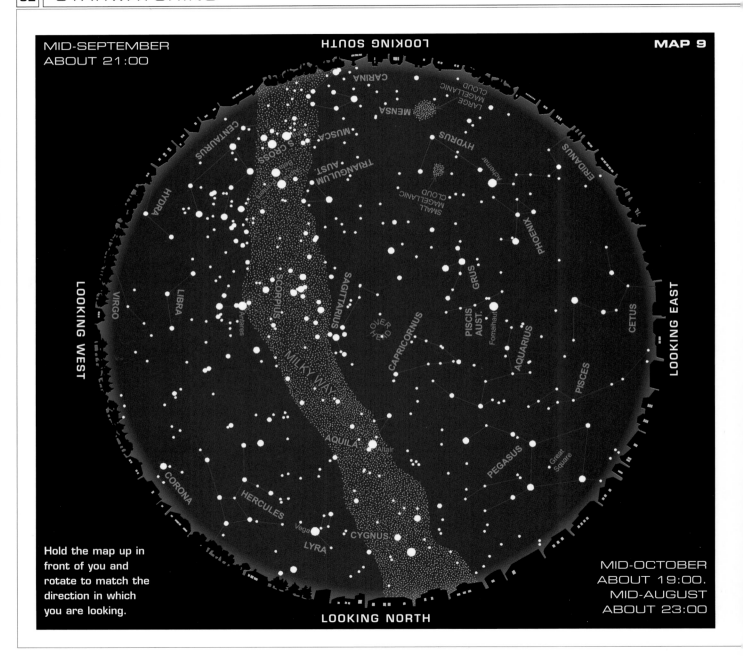

MID-SEPTEMBER
ABOUT 21:00

LOOKING SOUTH

MAP 9

LOOKING WEST

LOOKING EAST

Hold the map up in
front of you and
rotate to match the
direction in which
you are looking.

LOOKING NORTH

MID-OCTOBER
ABOUT 19:00.
MID-AUGUST
ABOUT 23:00

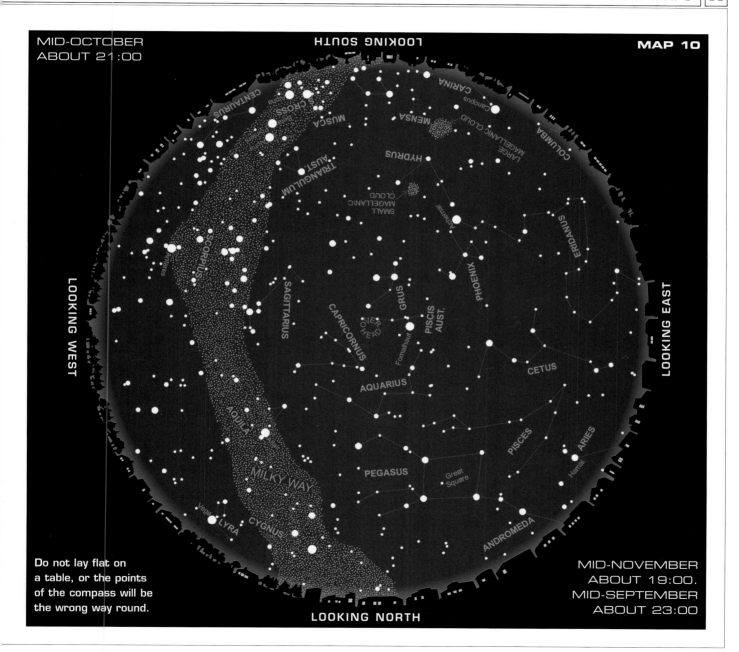

LOOKING SOUTH

LOOKING WEST

LOOKING EAST

CENTAURUS

S. CROSS

MUSCA

CARINA

Canopus

MENSA

LARGE MAGELLANIC CLOUD

COLUMBA

TRIANGULUM AUST.

HYDRUS

SMALL MAGELLANIC CLOUD

Achernar

ERIDANUS

SCORPIUS

Antares

PHOENIX

SAGITTARIUS

CAPRICORNUS

OVER HEAD

GRUS

PISCIS AUST.

Fomalhaut

CETUS

AQUILA

Altair

AQUARIUS

PISCES

ARIES

Hamal

MILKY WAY

PEGASUS

Great Square

Vega LYRA

CYGNUS

ANDROMEDA

Do not lay flat on
a table, or the points
of the compass will be
the wrong way round.

LOOKING NORTH

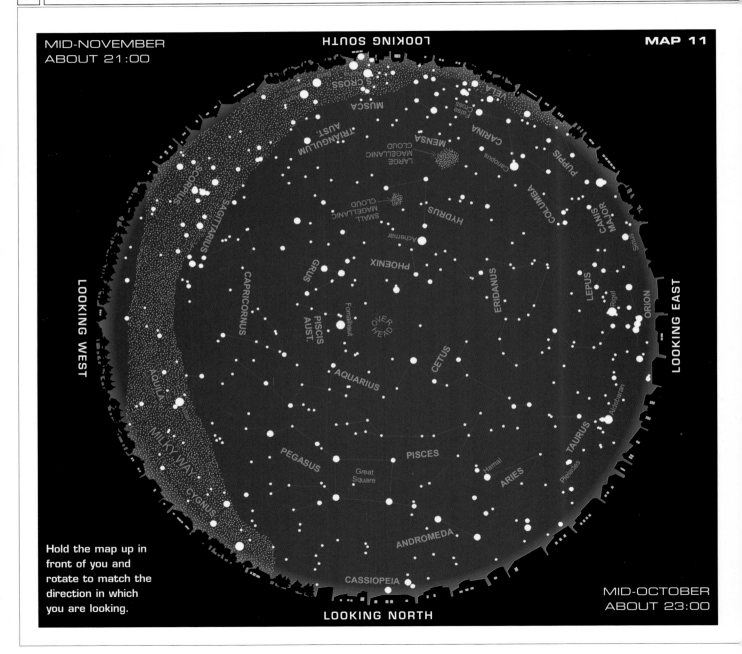

MID-NOVEMBER
ABOUT 21:00

LOOKING WEST

LOOKING EAST

Hold the map up in
front of you and
rotate to match the
direction in which
you are looking.

MID-OCTOBER
ABOUT 23:00

LOOKING NORTH

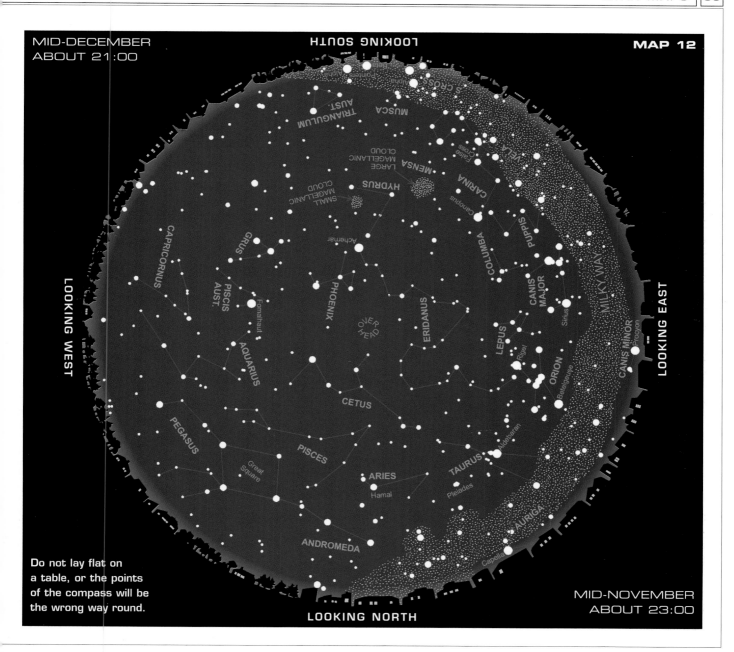

MID-DECEMBER
ABOUT 21:00

LOOKING SOUTH

MAP 12

LOOKING WEST

LOOKING EAST

Do not lay flat on
a table, or the points
of the compass will be
the wrong way round.

MID-NOVEMBER
ABOUT 23:00

LOOKING NORTH

Index